A
LITERARY
Book of Days

AMERICAN
VOICES

A
LITERARY
Book of Days

⸎

AMERICAN
VOICES

Library of Congress

Phaidon Universe
New York

Cover illustrations:

Top row, left to right: Samuel Clemens (Mark Twain),
  Carson McCullers, Ralph Waldo Emerson
Second row: Langston Hughes
Third row, left to right: e. e. cummings, Fannie Hurst,
  H. L. Mencken
Bottom row, left to right: Tennessee Williams,
  Vachel Lindsay

The July 29 illustration is by George Herriman
from *The Life and Times of Archy and Mehitabel*
by Don Marquis, copyright 1927, 1930, 1933,
1935, 1950 by Doubleday, a division of Bantam,
Doubleday, Dell Publishing Group, Inc. Used by
permission of the publisher.

Published in the United States of America in 1990
by Phaidon Universe
381 Park Avenue South, New York, NY 10016

90 91 92 93 94 / 10 9 8 7 6 5 4 3 2 1

Printed in the United States of America

ISBN 0-87663-699-7

Compilers: Margaret E. Wagner and Susan Sharp,
  Library of Congress, Publishing Office,
  with thanks to Michael Thompson
Editor: Dorothy R. Caeser
Designer: Christina Bliss

The Library of Congress, the world's largest library, is a unique symbol of civilization, learning, and literary culture. Among the Library's foremost roles is that of the national library of the United States. As such, and as this country's copyright repository, it is natural for its comprehensive Americana collections to be the best known and most heavily used. These collections reflect the scope and diversity of American imagination, art, and intellectual curiosity. They contain materials that range from the sublime to the ridiculous, and in combination reveal a nation rich in creativity, one capable of expressing, vividly, the many facets of its soul.

It is the richness and diversity of America's literary history that we endeavor to point out in this book of days. We remember here the famous—and the not so famous. Poets, novelists, essayists, columnists, playwrights, humorists, and scholars are included. It is *not* a comprehensive listing—many excellent reference works are devoted to that never-ending and monumental task. It *is* a celebration of the vast chorus of voices that make American literature sing.

The Library's own celebration of literature, and particularly American literature, is perpetual and kinetic. The core of its collections is the personal library of Thomas Jefferson—from whose keen and well-schooled intellect sprang that most celebrated American document, the Declaration of Independence. The three Library buildings themselves—most particularly the splendid original building, now named for Jefferson—are filled with architectural embellishments celebrating authors and the life of the mind.

Many Librarians of Congress have been men of letters—among them George Watterston, Ainsworth Rand Spofford, Archibald MacLeish, Daniel J. Boorstin, and the current Librarian, James H. Billington. Writers such as Paul Dunbar—who gave the first poetry reading in the Library's history—have been members of the Library staff. A consultantship in poetry was established in 1937, and today the Librarian of Congress names the Poet Laureate of the United States, who also serves as Consultant in Poetry to the Library. The Library hosts literary lectures, poetry readings, and other literary events. It produces its own publications, and it works through such programs as Honorary Consultants in American Letters and the activities of the Center for the Book in the Library of Congress to stimulate public interest in books, reading, and the written word.

As you peruse this book of days and record your own important events and anniversaries in it, I hope you will appreciate anew the richness of our literary heritage. Perhaps our little notes on who is who and did what will lead you to discover a writer you had not known or a book you will come to treasure. Such adventures keep the world of books forever new.

John Y. Cole
Director, The Center for the Book
in the Library of Congress

1897 Biographer Catherine Drinker Bowen, author of *Miracle at Philadelphia*, is born in Haverford, Pennsylvania.

1919 Reclusive novelist and short story writer Jerome David Salinger, whose first book, *The Catcher in the Rye*, becomes a classic, is born in New York City.

1894 Robert Nathan—author of *Portrait of Jennie*, *The Bishop's Wife*, and some two dozen other novels—is born in New York City.

1920 Ubiquitous writer, editor, and biochemist Isaac Asimov—author of *The Foundation Trilogy* and over 200 other books—is born in Petrovichi, Russia.

1886 Poet John Gould Fletcher, awarded the Pulitzer Prize in 1939 for his *Selected Poems*, is born in Little Rock, Arkansas.

1841 Seaman Herman Melville sails on the whaling ship *Acushnet*, beginning a 3-year voyage that will provide him with material for almost all of his novels and sea stories.

1938 In his annual report for 1937, Librarian of Congress Herbert Putnam notes that Joseph Auslander has been named the Library's first Consultant in Poetry. Subsequent Consultants will include Louise Bogan, Robert Lowell, Elizabeth Bishop, Randall Jarrell, Robert Frost, Stephen Spender, Stanley Kunitz, Maxine Kumin, Gwendolyn Brooks, and Howard Nemerov.

1883 Essayist and poet Max Eastman, author of *The Enjoyment of Poetry* and *The Enjoyment of Laughter*, is born in Canandaigua, New York.

Elizabeth Bishop in the Poetry Office at the Library of Congress, 1950.

Carl Sandburg, L. Quincy Mumford (then Librarian of Congress), and Robert Frost at the Library, May 1960.

1878 Poet Carl Sandburg, whose work celebrated the spirit and landscape of America, is born in Galesburg, Illinois. "A poet explains for us what for him is poetry by what he presents to us in his poems . . .There is no escape. There stands the work of the man, the woman, who wrought it. We go to it, read it, look at it, perhaps go back to it many a time, and it is for each of us what we make of it."

Zora Neale Hurston sometime between 1935 and 1943. Prints and Photographs Division.

1903 Folklorist, novelist, and short story writer Zora Neale Hurston is born in Eatonville, Florida.

1896 The first edition of the *Boston Cooking School Cook Book* is published by Fannie Farmer.

1881 John Gneisenau Neihardt, poet, critic, and author of *Black Elk Speaks* —which for the first time revealed the inner world of an American Indian holy man—is born near Sharpsburg, Illinois.

W *illiam James. Photo by* *Alice Boughton. Prints* *and Photographs Division.*

1887 Poet Robinson Jeffers is born in Pittsburgh.

1892 Historical biographer Dumas Malone, author of the multi-volume *Jefferson and His Time*, is born in Coldwater, Mississippi.

1776 Thomas Paine issues *Common Sense*, a 47-page pamphlet containing the first demand for complete independence for the American colonies:

"This new world hath been the asylum for the persecuted lovers of civil and religious liberty in every part of Europe. Hither have they fled, not from the tender embraces of the mother, but from the cruelty of the monster; and it is so far true of England, that the same tyranny which drove the first emigrants from home, pursues their descendants still."

1842 Philosopher and psychologist William James, brother of novelist Henry James, is born in New York City. "The moral flabbiness born of the exclusive worship of the bitch-goddess *success*," James wrote to H. G. Wells in 1906, "that— with the squalid cash interpretation put on the word success—is our national disease."

1825 Bayard Taylor, author of popular travel books and novels and translator of Goethe, is born in Kennett Square, Pennsylvania.

JANUARY

12

1876 Jack London is born in San Francisco. Exactly 17 years later on this date London will embark as a seaman on a 7-month voyage aboard the sealing schooner *Sophie Sutherland*, a voyage that will provide material from which he will build his novel *The Sea Wolf*.

1834 Horatio Alger—who portrayed American life in over 70 books (most of them stories for boys) as rigorous and fair and full of promise—is born in Revere, Massachusetts.

1890 Essayist, novelist, and commentator Elmer Holmes Davis—director of the Office of War Information during World War II—is born in Aurora, Indiana.

JANUARY

13

1901 Alfred Bertram Guthrie, Jr., author of *The Big Sky*, is born in Bedford, Indiana.

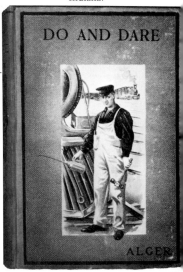

A 1905 edition from among the 119 published works of Horatio Alger. Rare Book and Special Collections Division.

JANUARY

14

1896 Novelist John Dos Passos, author of the *U.S.A.* trilogy, is born in Chicago.

1899 "The Man with the Hoe," a poem by California schoolteacher Edwin Markham depicting a farmer brutalized by forces he could not control or understand, is published in the San Francisco *Examiner*. It is extensively reprinted and quickly becomes the most popular poem in the United States.

JANUARY

15

1942 Librarian of Congress Archibald MacLeish announces that Thomas Mann, ''whose devotion to the cause of democracy led him to self-imposed exile from Nazi Germany,'' has joined the Library staff as consultant in German literature.

Archibald MacLeish at his desk in the office of the Librarian of Congress, ca. 1941.

1706 Writer, printer, philosopher, and statesman Benjamin Franklin is born in Boston. In *Poor Richard's Almanac* Franklin once wrote: ''If you would not be forgotten, as soon as you are dead and rotten, either write things worth reading, or do things worth the writing.'' A man who knew good advice when he wrote it, Franklin took *both* roads to remembrance.

1809 Edgar Allan Poe—poet, creator of the first modern detective story, and dreamer of troubling dreams—is born in Boston. ''With me poetry has not been a purpose, but a passion; and the passions should be held in reverence: they must not—they cannot at will be excited, with an eye to the paltry compensations, or the more paltry commendations, of mankind.''

1887 Journalist, drama critic, writer, and occasional actor Alexander Woollcott is born in Phalanx, New Jersey.

JANUARY
20

1961 Robert Frost, 76, prevented by glaring sunshine from reading lines he had composed especially for the occasion, recites his poem "The Gift Outright" at President John F. Kennedy's inauguration.

Robert Frost making a recording for the blind in the Library of Congress recording lab, 1959.

JANUARY
21

1904 Reclusive poet and critic Richard P. Blackmur is born, probably in Massachusetts.

1789 The first American novel, *The Power or the Triumph of Nature* by William Hill Brown—a book the author hoped would "Expose the dangerous Consequences of Seduction"—is published in Boston.

JANUARY
22

1893 Journalist, novelist, mystery writer, and playwright Fulton Oursler—best known for his retelling of the New Testament in *The Greatest Story Ever Told*—is born in Baltimore.

JANUARY
23

1862 Patrician novelist Edith Wharton, author of *The Age of Innocence* and *Ethan Frome*, is born in New York City. "I was never allowed to read the popular American children's books of my day because, as my mother said, the children spoke bad English *without the author's knowing it.*"

JANUARY

24

JANUARY

25

JANUARY

26

1831 Mary Mapes Dodge, author of *Hans Brinker, or The Silver Skates*, is born in New York City.

JANUARY

27

JANUARY
28

1831 Edgar Allan Poe (who hadn't really wanted to be there in the first place) is court martialled at the United States Military Academy at West Point, New York, because of conspicuous misconduct. He will be formally dismissed from the Academy on March 6.

JANUARY
29

1737 Thomas Paine, whose pamphlets will contribute so forcefully to the making of the American Revolution, is born in Thetford, Norfolk, England.

1845 "The Raven" ("Take thy beak from out my heart, and take thy form from off my door!"/ Quoth the Raven, "Nevermore.") appears in the New York *Evening Mirror*, bringing renown to its author, Edgar Allan Poe.

1912 Historian Barbara Tuchman, author of *The Guns of August* and *The March of Folly*, is born in New York City.

JANUARY
30

1815 Congress purchases Thomas Jefferson's 6,487-volume personal library, thus re-establishing the Library of Congress, which was destroyed by the British during the War of 1812. The cost is $23,950, and two-thirds of the sum is sent directly to Jefferson's creditors.

JANUARY
31

1872 Popular novelist Zane Grey, whose 54 novels made his name almost synonymous with the Old West, is born in Zanesville(!), Ohio.

1905 Novelist and short story writer John O'Hara, author of *Appointment in Samarra*, *A Rage to Live*, and the *Pal Joey* sketches, is born in Pottsville, Pennsylvania.

1915 Philosopher and poet Thomas Merton is born in France.

1923 Norman Mailer is born in Long Branch, New Jersey.

*W*oodcut by *Antonio Frasconi from* The Face of Edgar Allan Poe *(opposite). Rare Book and Special Collections Division.*

FEBRUARY

1

1811 Delia Slater Bacon is born in Tallmadge, Ohio. The author of *Tales of the Puritans* and *The Bridge of Fort Edward* is best remembered for developing the theory that Shakespeare's plays were actually written by 17th-century English philosopher Francis Bacon and a few of his friends.

1902 Poet Langston Hughes is born in Joplin, Missouri. He will become the only black writer of his time in the U.S. to live entirely from his earnings as a writer.

1904 Humorist Sidney Joseph Perelman—a practitioner of the "screwball wit" school of writing who once said that he considered James Joyce "*the* great comic writer of our time" —is born in Brooklyn, New York.

1923 Poet and novelist James Dickey, author of *Deliverance* and Library of Congress Consultant in Poetry, 1966–68, is born in Atlanta, Georgia.

Langston Hughes, 1943. Photo by Gordon Parks. Prints and Photographs Division.

FEBRUARY

2

1874 Gertrude Stein—writer and mentor of writers, a favorite student of psychologist-philosopher William James, and for four years a student of medicine at Johns Hopkins University—is born in Allegheny, Pennsylvania.

1907 James A. Michener, whose *Tales of the South Pacific* will win the 1947 Pulitzer Prize—and will shortly thereafter be transformed on Broadway into *South Pacific*—is born in New York City. "I have one bit of advice to beginning writers," Michener wrote: "be sure your novel is read by Rodgers and Hammerstein."

FEBRUARY

3

1883 Clarence Edward Mulford, writer of Western stories and creator of Hopalong Cassidy, is born in Streator, Illinois.

1904 Novelist Mackinlay Kantor, author of *Andersonville* and *Long Remember*, is born in Webster City, Iowa.

1921 Betty Friedan, whose 1963 analysis of *The Feminine Mystique* will become a pillar of the modern women's movement, is born in Peoria, Illinois.

FEBRUARY

4

1914 William Burroughs, author of *Naked Lunch*, is born in St. Louis, Missouri.

1945 *Life* magazine correspondent John Dos Passos enters Manila with the Sixth Army. Dos Passos's collected essays about World War II are published the following year in *Tour of Duty*.

1980 Lillian Hellman files a $2.5 million lawsuit against Mary McCarthy for defamation of character after Ms. McCarthy calls Ms. Hellman a "dishonest writer" on a January 25 television show.

FEBRUARY

5

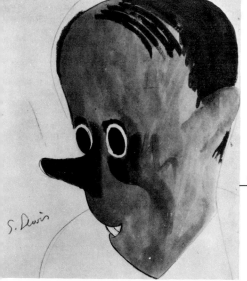

FEBRUARY

6

Sinclair Lewis by Covarrubias. Prints and Photographs Division.

FEBRUARY

7

1907 Sinclair Lewis—author of *Main Street*, *Babbitt*, and *Elmer Gantry*, and the first American to receive the Nobel Prize for Literature—is born in Sauk Centre, Minnesota.

1867 Children's book author Laura Ingalls Wilder, writer of the "Little House" books, is born in Pepin, Wisconsin.

FEBRUARY
8

1911 Poet Elizabeth Bishop, Library of Congress Consultant in Poetry, 1949–50, is born in Worcester, Massachusetts.

1874 Poet, critic, and biographer *(John Keats)* Amy Lowell is born in Brookline, Massachusetts.

FEBRUARY
9

1901 Journalist Max Miller is born in Montana. Miller, who served in two world wars and Korea, wrote a number of books about his armed forces experiences. "I always think that whatever isn't recorded for the public," he said, "hasn't happened."

FEBRUARY
10

1949 Death of a Salesman by Arthur Miller opens at the Morosco Theatre in New York City. The play receives the New York Drama Critics Award, the Pulitzer Prize, and the distinction of being the first play chosen as a Book-of-the-Month Club selection.

FEBRUARY
11

W*riter, scientist, and educator Booker T Washington, 1906 (opposite). Prints and Photographs Division.*

Engraved by Geo. E. Perine, N.Y. for the Eclectic, after Drawing by C.N. Cochin, 1777.

Benj Franklin

1741 The first American magazine, the short lived *American Magazine, or a Monthly View of the Political State of the British Colonies,* edited by John Webbe, is published in Philadelphia.

1882 Drama critic and author George Jean Nathan is born in Ft. Wayne, Indiana.

1945 Prisoner of war Kurt Vonnegut survives the fire-bombing of Dresden by British and American planes with other POWs locked in a meat-storage cellar under a slaughterhouse. Over 20 years later this experience emerges in the novel *Slaughterhouse Five.*

Benjamin Franklin, from a 1777 drawing by C. N. Cochin (opposite). Prints and Photographs Division.

FEBRUARY
16

1838 Historian and man of letters Henry Brooks Adams is born in Boston. In his classic work, *The Education of Henry Adams*, he will write: "The difference is slight, to the influence of an author, whether he is read by five hundred readers, or by five hundred thousand; if he can select the five hundred, he reaches the five hundred thousand."

1886 Critic and biographer Van Wyck Brooks, author of *The Ordeal of Mark Twain* and *The Writer in America*, is born in Plainfield, New Jersey.

FEBRUARY
17

1879 Novelist Dorothy Canfield Fisher, among whose works are *The Deepening Stream* and *Vermont Tradition*, is born in Lawrence, Kansas.

1929 Chaim Potok is born in New York City.

FEBRUARY
18

1909 Wallace Stegner, essayist, biographer, and Pulitzer Prize-winning author of novels of western American life *(The Big Rock Candy Mountain, Angle of Repose)*, is born on a farm near Lake Milles, Iowa.

1931 Editor, novelist, and teacher Toni Morrison, author of *Song of Solomon*, is born in Lorain, Ohio. Remembering her avid youthful reading of the works of Flaubert, Austen, Tolstoy, and their ilk she will say: "Those books were not written for a little black girl in Lorain, Ohio, but they were so magnificently done that I got them anyway.... when I wrote my first novel years later, I wanted to capture that same specificity about the nature and feeling of the culture *I* grew up in."

FEBRUARY
19

1903 Novelist and short story writer Kay Boyle is born in St. Paul, Minnesota.

1927 Carson McCullers, author of *The Member of the Wedding, The Ballad of the Sad Cafe*, and *The Heart is a Lonely Hunter*, is born in Columbus, Georgia.

Carson McCullers, from a painting by Henry Varnum Poor, ca. 1946. Print and Photographs Division

1676 Mrs. Mary Rowlandson is captured by a Wampanoug war party and remains their prisoner for 2½ months. Her account of this ordeal, *The Sovereignty & Goodness of God, Together with the Faithfulness of his Promises Displayed: Being a Narrative of the Captivity and Restauration of Mrs. Mary Rowlandson*, published in 1682, becomes the first American prose best seller.

1893 Journalist and novelist Russel Crouse, who collaborated with Howard Lindsay on such plays as *Life with Father* and *The Sound of Music*, is born in Findlay, Ohio.

FEBRUARY

20

1828 The first newspaper in an Indian language, the *Cherokee Phoenix*, is published in Echota, Georgia, following the arrival on this date of a printing press at the headquarters of the Cherokee Council. Written and printed in the Cherokee language based on letter symbols that had been created by the Cherokee leader Seqoyah, the paper is edited by another Cherokee, Elias Boudinot.

1907 Poet W. H. Auden —who will become an American citizen in 1940, drawn by America's openness and lack of tradition— is born in York, England.

FEBRUARY

21

1892 Poet Edna St. Vincent Millay, winner of the 1923 Pulitzer Prize for *The Harp-Weaver*, is born in Rockland, Maine.

1819 Poet, essayist, and diplomat James Russell Lowell—who believed that "Solitude is as needful to the imagination as society is wholesome for the character"—is born in Cambridge, Massachusetts.

1925 Author and artist Edward Gorey is born in New York City.

FEBRUARY

22

1868 Editor, teacher, theorist, and novelist William Edward Burghardt DuBois is born in Great Barrington, Massachusetts. "Herein lies the tragedy of the age: not that men are poor—all men know something of poverty; not that men are wicked—who is good? Not that men are ignorant—what is truth? Nay, but that men know so little of men."

1904 Historian and journalist William L. Shirer, author of *Berlin Diary* and *The Rise and Fall of the Third Reich*, is born in Chicago.

FEBRUARY

23

FEBRUARY

24

1909   Versatile and voluminous author August Derleth—writer of poetry, short stories, novels, mysteries, and books for young people—is born in Sauk City, Wisconsin.

FEBRUARY

25

1907 Playwright Mary Coyle Chase is born in Denver, Colorado. Her most enduring and endearing contribution to American theater is the Pulitzer Prize-winning play *Harvey*, about the magic that occurs when imaginative alcoholic Elwood P. Dowd is be-friended by an invisible 6-foot rabbit. The character Dowd may have been inspired by something the playwright's mother told her when she was a child: "Never be unkind or indifferent to a person others say is crazy. Often they have deep wisdom."

FEBRUARY

26

1986 Librarian of Congress Daniel J. Boorstin appoints Robert Penn Warren Poet Laureate, Consultant in Poetry—thus making Warren the first official Poet Laureate of the United States.

R*obert Penn Warren reads at the Library of Congress, December 1955.*

FEBRUARY

27

1807 Henry Wadsworth Longfellow—whose poems include "Evangeline," "The Song of Hiawatha," and "Paul Revere's Ride"—is born in Portland, Maine. "Music," wrote Longfellow, "is the universal language of mankind—poetry their universal pastime and delight."

1902 John Steinbeck, who will win the 1962 Nobel Prize for Literature, is born in Salinas, California.

1904 James Thomas Farrell, author of the Studs Lonigan novels, is born in Chicago.

1979 Historian Barbara Tuchman is elected president of the American Academy and Institute of Arts and Letters, the first woman to achieve that office.

1893 Novelist and dramatist Ben Hecht, who collaborated with Charles MacArthur on *The Front Page*, is born in New York City.

Henry Wadsworth Long-fellow, from the May 1886 Century *magazine. Prints and Photographs Division.*

MARCH
1

1914 Novelist Ralph Ellison is born in Oklahoma City, Oklahoma.

1917 Robert Lowell, Jr.— Pulitzer Prize winner and Library of Congress Consultant in Poetry, 1947–48 —is born in Boston.

1921 Scholar, translator, and second Poet Laureate of the United States Richard Wilbur is born in New York City. "One does not use poetry for its major purposes, as a means of organizing oneself and the world, until one's world somehow gets out of hand. A general cataclysm is not required; the disorder must be personal and may be wholly so, but poetry, to be vital, does seem to need a periodic acquaintance with the threat of Chaos."

1837 Critic, novelist, editor, and writer of travel books William Dean Howells, a champion of realism in American literature, is born in Martin's Ferry, Ohio.

William Dean Howells, ca. 1898. Prints and Photographs Division.

MARCH
2

1942 Novelist John Irving, author of *The World According to Garp,* is born in Exeter, New Hampshire.

MARCH
3

1926 Pulitzer Prize-winning poet James Merrill is born in New York City.

1880 Channing Pollock —playwright, essayist, and novelist—is born in Washington, DC. Pollock will also write songs, including "My Man," which will be popularized by Fanny Brice.

1904 Theodor Seuss Geisel, the renowned "Dr. Seuss," is born in Springfield, Massachusetts.

1870 Novelist Frank Norris, author of *McTeague*, is born in Chicago.

Ring Lardner by Covarrubias. Prints and Photographs Division.

1885 Ring Lardner, journalist and short story writer known for his comic writing—yet once called "Perhaps the greatest and sincerest pessimist America has produced"—is born in Niles, Michigan.

1935 Former Supreme Court Justice Oliver Wendell Holmes dies at the age of 94, bequeathing his private library to the Library of Congress.

1980 Naturalized United States citizen Marguerite Yourcenar becomes the first woman to be elected to the French Academy.

MARCH
8

1890 Gene Fowler—
journalist, novelist, and
biographer *(Beau James:
The Life and Times of Jim-
my Walker; Good Night,
Sweet Prince)*—is born in
Denver, Colorado.

MARCH
9

1918 Mickey Spillane,
master of violent detective
fiction and creator of the
hard-boiled Mike Hammer,
is born in Brooklyn, New
York.

MARCH
10

*"Inherited ideas are curi-
ous things." Illustration by
Dan Beard from the first
edition of Mark Twain's* A
Connecticut Yankee in
King Arthur's Court, *1889.
Cabinet of American Illustration, Prints and Photographs Division.*

MARCH
11

1880 Mark Twain sends
his nephew to "burrow a
little" in the Library of
Congress, "a grand literary
storehouse."

1922 Jack Kerouac is born in Lowell, Massachusetts.

1928 Playwright Edward Albee, author of *Who's Afraid of Virginia Woolf?*, is born in Washington, DC.

1892 Janet Flanner (Genêt), who for half a century was Paris correspondent to *The New Yorker*, is born in Boston

1918 Critic and biographer Richard Ellmann is born in Highland Park, Michigan.

MARCH

16

1875 Dramatist and poet Percy MacKaye, for whom the first fellowship in creative literature in the United States will be founded in Miami in 1900, is born in New York. MacKaye will write a variety of works, many of them reflecting his intense interest in folk literature and the preservation of native American arts.

1937 Correspondent Ernest Hemingway arrives in Spain to cover the Civil War. While there, he will meet fellow correspondent, and future wife, Martha Gellhorn and gather experiences that will generate the novel *For Whom the Bell Tolls*, as well as a play and a number of short stories.

MARCH

17

1894 Paul Green, novelist and Pulitzer Prize-winning playwright, is born on a farm near Lillington, North Carolina. In 1937 Green will see his "symphonic drama," *The Lost Colony*, produced on Roanoke Island, North Carolina, where it is such a resounding success that it is staged for two months every year thereafter.

MARCH

18

1892 Poet Robert Peter Tristram Coffin is born in Brunswick, Maine. "Among my definitions of poetry are these: Poetry is the art of making people feel well about life; poetry is saying the best one can about life; poetry is the art of putting different kinds of good things together: men and plows, boys and whistles, hounds and deer, sorrow and sympathy, life and death."

1932 John Updike is born in Shillington, Pennsylvania.

1933 Phillip Roth, author of *Goodbye Columbus*, is born in Newark, New Jersey.

MARCH

19

"So the woggle-bug strutted proudly along the street." Illustration by Ike Morgan from The Woggle-Bug Book *by L. Frank Baum, 1905 (opposite). Rare Book and Special Collections Division.*

So the Woggle-Bug strutted proudly along the street.

MARCH
20

1852 Harriet Beecher
Stowe's provocative anti-
slavery novel *Uncle Tom's
Cabin* is published.

MARCH
21

MARCH
22

1857 Cookery expert
and cookbook editor
Fannie Farmer is born in
Boston.

1939 Richard Hallibur-
ton, author of such romantic travel books as *The
Royal Road to Romance*
and *The Glorious Adven-
ture,* is lost in the Pacific
while attempting to sail a
75-foot Chinese junk, the
Sea Dragon, from Hong
Kong to the San Francisco
World's Fair.

MARCH
23

1919 Poet Lawrence Ferlinghetti is born in Yonkers, New York.

1925 Flannery O'Connor is born in Savannah, Georgia.

1874 Robert Frost—who will be proclaimed "the voice of New England," and whose first book of poems, *A Boy's Will*, will be published in Old England—is born in San Francisco. "A poem begins with a lump in the throat; a homesickness or a lovesickness. It is a reaching-out toward expression; an effort to find fulfillment. A complete poem is one where an emotion has found its thought and the thought has found the words."

1908 Memoirist and humorist Betty MacDonald, author of *The Egg and I*, is born in Boulder, Colorado.

1911 Thomas Lanier (Tennessee) Williams is born in Columbus, Mississippi.

1913 Claiming he is innocent, writer Julian Hawthorne, only son of Nathaniel Hawthorne, is sent to prison for a year for misusing the mails. While inside, Hawthorne edits the prison paper, and after his release writes *The Subterranean Brotherhood*, an indictment of prison conditions.

Tennessee Williams. Photo by Fred Obringer. Prints and Photographs Division.

MARCH
27

1914 Short story writer and novelist Budd Schulberg, author of *What Makes Sammy Run?*, is born in New York City.

Nelson Algren, ca. 1951. Photo by Robert McCullough. Prints and Photographs Division.

MARCH
28

1793 Ethnologist, explorer, geologist, and writer Henry Rowe Schoolcraft —the first white man to translate American Indian poetry, and among the first to study Indian legend and religion—is born in Albany County, New York.

1909 Nelson Algren author of *The Man with th Golden Arm* and *A Wal on the Wild Side*, is born i Detroit, Michigan.

MARCH
29

1889 Producer, acto and playwright Howar Lindsay—who collaborate with Russel Crouse on *Li with Father* and the Puli zer Prize-winning politic comedy *State of the Unio* —is born in Waterforc New York.

MARCH
30

*Charles Scribner by Oliver
Herford, ca. 1914. Cabinet
of American Illustration,
Prints and Photographs
Division.*

APRIL
1

1922 Historian William Manchester, author of *The Death of a President, American Caesar*, and *Goodbye Darkness*, is born in Attleboro, Massachusetts.

APRIL
2

APRIL
3

1783 Writer and diplomat Washington Irving—author of "Rip Van Winkle," "The Legend of Sleepy Hollow," and the satirical *A History of New York* which has been called "the first great book of comic literature written by an American"—is born in New York City.

APRIL
4

1896 Playwright Robert E. Sherwood, three-time winner of the Pulitzer Prize for drama (for *Idiot's Delight, Abe Lincoln in Illinois*, and *There Shall Be No Night*) and one-time winner for history (*Roosevelt and Hopkins: An Intimate History*), is born in New Rochelle, New York.

1866 Journalist and author Lincoln Steffens is born in San Francisco.

1903 Novelist and short story writer Charles Reginald Jackson, author of *The Lost Weekend*, is born in Summit, New Jersey.

1931 Poet and short story writer Donald Barthelme is born in Philadelphia.

APRIL
9

1859 Mark Twain becomes a licensed pilot of Mississippi steamboats in the District of St. Louis.

APRIL
10

1827 Novelist, lawyer, soldier, and diplomat General Lew Wallace, author of *Ben-Hur*, is born in Brookville, Indiana.

APRIL
11

1908 Leo Rosten—humorist, political scientist, teacher, and creator of H*Y*M*A*N* K*A*P*L*A*N —is born in Lodz, Poland. "To pay my debts I began to write humorous sketches which the *New Yorker* published. I was now branded a humorist, and every time I opened my mouth there would be gales of laughter."

1916 Two drafts of President Abraham Lincoln's Gettysburg Address, believed to be the original and second drafts, are presented to the United States Government by the descendants of John Hay and placed in the custody of the Library of Congress.

APRIL
12

1919 Beverly Cleary creator of Henry Huggins his dog Ribsy, Beezus and Ramona, and the concep of the rodent motorcyclist is born in McMinnville Oregon.

1909 Pulitzer Prize-winning novelist and short story writer Eudora Welty —author of *Delta Wedding* and *The Robber Bridegroom*—is born in Jackson, Mississippi. About the process of writing, Ms. Welty will say: "I certainly never think of who is going to read [what I'm writing]. I don't think of myself either—at least, I don't believe I do. I just think of what it is that I'm writing. That's enough to do."

1743 Thomas Jefferson is born in Shadwell, Virginia.

APRIL

13

APRIL

14

1828 The first edition of Noah Webster's *American Dictionary of the English Language*—which includes 12,000 new words that have never been included in any dictionary—s published.

1843 Novelist Henry James—about whom Mrs. Henry Adams will say, "Henry James chews more than he bites off"—is born in New York City.

APRIL

15

Henry James. Photo by Alice Boughton. Prints and Photographs Division.

1895 Portrait busts of Demosthenes, Emerson, Washington Irving, Goethe, Franklin, Macaulay, Hawthorne, Sir Walter Scott, and Dante are hoisted into place across the west front of the new Library of Congress Building.

APRIL

16

APRIL

17

1897 Novelist and playwright Thornton Wilder—among whose works are *The Bridge of San Luis Rey, Our Town*, and *The Skin of Our Teeth*—is born in Madison, Wisconsin.

Ambrose Bierce, from a painting by J. H. E. Parkington, ca. 1928. Prints and Photographs Division.

APRIL

18

APRIL

19

1871 Short story writer and novelist Melville Davison Post—best known for a series of ingenious detective tales featuring his fictitious Uncle Abner, a Virginia squire contemporary to Thomas Jefferson —is born near Clarksburg, West Virginia.

1861 Ambrose Bierce, whose acidic commentaries on human behavior are etched on the pages of *The Devil's Dictionary*, enlists in the Union Army and begins almost four years of service during which he is wounded, commended for heroism, and promoted several times. Bierce's Civil War experience will color his life, and his writing, thereafter.

Ambrose Bierce title page. General collections.

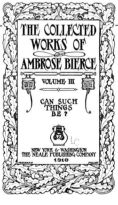

APRIL

20

1946 British writer W. Somerset Maugham presents a manuscript of his novel *Of Human Bondage* to the United States and the Library of Congress to acknowledge "the kindness and generosity with which you received the women and children of my country when in fear of a German invasion they came to America."

1838 Scottish-American naturalist John Muir is born in Dunbar, Scotland.

1910 Mark Twain, 79, dies in Redding, Connecticut, the end of his life marked, as was its beginning, by an appearance of Halley's Comet.

APRIL

21

APRIL

22

1874 Novelist Ellen Glasgow, whose work was once characterized as "a perpetual rebellion against hypocrisy," is born in Richmond, Virginia.

APRIL

23

1852 Poet Edwin Markham, author of "The Man with the Hoe" and one of the writers of the Golden Age of California literature, is born in Oregon City, Oregon.

1800 President John Adams approves an "act to make provision for the removal and accommodation of the Government of the United States," which establishes the Library of Congress.

1905 Robert Penn Warren—winner of Pulitzer Prizes for both poetry and fiction; Library of Congress Consultant in Poetry, 1944–45; and the first Poet Laureate, Consultant in Poetry at the Library, 1986–87—is born in Guthrie, Kentucky.

APRIL

24

APRIL 25

1898 William Sydney Porter enters the Ohio State Penitentiary to begin serving a 5-year sentence for embezzlement. While in prison, Porter will write several stories under various pen names; the one he will keep, O. Henry, is probably borrowed from Orrin Henry, a prison guard.

1914 Novelist Ross Franklin Lockridge, Jr. is born in Bloomington, Indiana. His only book, *Raintree County*—a 1,066-page story that takes place entirely on July 4, 1892—will be published in 1948 and become an immediate and phenomenal success, perhaps a contributing factor to the author's suicide on March 6 of that year.

APRIL 26

John James Audubon, 1861 engraving from a painting by Chappel. Prints and Photographs Division.

1785 Ornithologist John James Audubon, author of *The Birds of America* and *Delineations of American Scenery and Character*, is born at Les Cayes, Santo Domingo.

1834 Humorist, newspaper editor, and lecturer Artemus Ward (the pen name of Charles Farrar Browne) is born near Waterford, Maine. Ward will be an important influence on Mark Twain and other American humorists of his time.

1862 In a letter to Thomas Wentworth Higginson, Emily Dickinson speaks of one catalyst for her poetry: "I had a terror since September, I could tell to none; and so I sing, as the boy does of the burying ground, because I am afraid."

1893 Anita Loos, author of *Gentlemen Prefer Blondes*, is born in Sisson, California.

1914 Pulitzer Prize-winning novelist Bernard Malamud, author of *The Natural* and *The Fixer*, is born in Brooklyn, New York.

APRIL 27

1932 Returning from Mexico, where he had gone on a Guggenheim Fellowship, poet Hart Crane, 34, commits suicide by jumping from the *S.S. Orizaba* into the sea about 300 miles north of Havana.

1926 Harper Lee, author
of *To Kill a Mockingbird*,
is born in Monroeville,
Alabama.

1877 Alice B. Toklas is
born in San Francisco.

1888 Critic, educator,
and poet John Crowe Ran-
som is born in Pulaski,
Tennessee.

‘ ‘ God have mercy on the sinner
Who must write with no dinner,
No gravy and no grub,
No pewter and no pub,
No belly and no bowels,
Only consonants and vowels.’ ’

T*itle page,* McGuffey's
Third Eclectic Reader,
1879. General collections.

MAY

1

1923 Joseph Heller, author of *Catch-22*, is born in Brooklyn, New York.

MAY

2

1801 The first books (152 works in 740 volumes) and maps (3) for the new Library of Congress arrive in Washington, DC and are stored in the office of the Secretary of the Senate.

MAY

3

1853 Edgar Watson Howe, author of the classic novel *The Story of a Country Town*, a powerful and realistic portrayal of a Middle Western small town, is born in Treaty, Indiana. "There is nothing so well known as that we should not expect something for nothing—but we all do and call it Hope."

1912 Poet, novelist, and memoirist May Sarton is born in Wondelgem, Belgium.

1913 William Motter Inge, whose play *Picnic* won the 1953 Pulitzer Prize for drama, is born in Independence, Kansas.

MAY

4

1865 Elizabeth Cochrane Seaman, better known as the muckraking and stunt-pulling journalist "Nellie Bly," is born in Cochrane Mills, Pennsylvania. Ms. Bly's most famous exploits will be having herself committed to an insane asylum and then exposing the conditions therein, and going around the world in 72 days, 6 hours, 11 minutes—thereby beating the record set by the hero of Jules Verne's novel *Around the World in 80 Days.*

1890 Prolific novelist and essayist Christopher Darlington Morley, among whose works is *Kitty Foyle,* is born in Haverford, Pennsylvania.

1926 In a letter declining the 1926 Pulitzer Prize for his novel *Arrowsmith,* Sinclair Lewis writes: "Every compulsion is put upon writers to become safe, polite, obedient, and sterile. In protest, I declined election to the National Institute of Arts and Letters some years ago, and now I must decline the Pulitzer Prize." Four years later, Lewis becomes the first American to be honored with the Nobel Prize for Literature, and accepts the award.

Sinclair Lewis, ca. 1930. Prints and Photographs Division.

1892 Archibald MacLeish is born in Glencoe, Illinois. MacLeish dated the beginning of his life from 1923, when, leaving the practice of law, he decided to take a chance on living by poetry alone. Yet his career thereafter, while infused with poetry, also included the writing of plays and appointments as Librarian of Congress (1939–44) and Assistant Secretary of State under Franklin D. Roosevelt.

Archibald MacLeish.

1771 Poet Phillis Wheatley sails for London, where she is introduced to British dignitaries and meets fellow American Ben Franklin. A book of her poetry, *Poems on Various Subjects, Religious and Moral,* the first book by a black American, is published in London in 1773.

1895 Preeminent literary critic and writer Edmund Wilson, who will stir lively controversies with his forthright views and forceful prose, is born in Red Bank, New Jersey.

1938 Thomas Pynchon, author of *Gravity's Rainbow* and *The Crying of Lot 49,* is born in Glen Cove, New York.

1898 Historian Ariel
Durant (Ida Kaufman) is
born in the Ukraine.

Joseph Pulitzer by Oliver
Herford. Cabinet of Amer
ican Illustration, Prints
and Photographs Division.

"Dorothy scolds the cowardly lion." Illustration by W. W. Denslow from The Wonderful Wizard of Oz *by L. Frank Baum, 1900. Rare Book and Special Collections Division.*

"You ought to be ashamed of yourself!"

MAY

13

MAY

14

1856 L. Frank Baum—author of *The Wonderful Wizard of Oz*, "the first distinctive attempt to construct a fairyland out of American materials"—is born in Chittenango, New York.

1890 Katherine Anne Porter, noted for her subtle and poetic prose, is born in Indian Creek, Texas. "I did not choose this vocation," Ms. Porter once said of writing, "and if I had any say in the matter, I would not of chosen it. . . . Yet for this vocation I was and am willing to live and die, and I consider very few other things of the slightest importance."

1904 Literary critic Clifton Fadiman is born in Brooklyn, New York.

1923 Carroll John Daly turns away from the gentleman investigator to introduce hard-boiled detective Terry Mack in his story "Three Gun Terry," published in *Black Mask* magazine. Mack shows his stripes in the first sentence: "My life is my own, and the opinions of others don't interest me; so don't form any, or if you do, keep them to yourself."

MAY

15

1912 Louis ("Studs") Terkel, author of *Hard Times*, *Working*, and *The Good War*, is born in New York City.

1914 Randall Jarrell, poet, critic—and Library of Congress Consultant in Poetry, 1956–58—is born in Nashville, Tennessee.

L. *Frank Baum, Chicago, 1908. Photo by Dana Hull.*

MAY

16

MAY
17

1906 Playwright John Patrick is born in Louisville, Kentucky. His best-known original work, *The Hasty Heart*, about a dying soldier who tries to keep the rest of the world at arm's length, stemmed from Patrick's experiences as an ambulance driver in World War II.

MAY
18

MAY
19

1930 Playwright Lorraine Hansberry, author of *A Raisin in the Sun*, is born in Chicago.

1890 American playwright Clyde Fitch begins his career with the hugely successful *Beau Brummell*.

1890 Historian and biographer Allan Nevins is born in Camp Point, Illinois.

MAY
20

1946 W. H. Auden becomes a United States citizen.

An early draft of Walt Whitman's "O Captain My Captain!" in the Library's Manuscript Division (opposite).

My Captain

The mortal voyage over, the gales the rocks and tempests

    pass'd   the prize we sought is won,

The ship I love comes home again, the sun is bright and clear, the sun breaks forth in splendor,

The port is close, the bells we hear, the

    As people all exulting.

While steady comes and enters straight the my

    wond'rous veteran vessel;

But O heart! heart! heart! you leave not

    the little spot,

Where on the deck my Captain lies — sleeping

    & dead.

            ss.   This verse only

O Captain! dearest Captain! wake up get

     & hear the bells;

Wake up & see the flag, flags, & see the

    flags a-flying; splendid sun

For you it is the cities shout — for you the

    shores are crowded;

For you the red-rose garlands, and the electric eyes

    of women;

O Captain! O my father! my arm I push

     breath you;

It is some Dream that on the deck

    You slumber pale, cold & dead.

MAY
21

1889 Novelist Frances Ormond Gaither is born in Somerville, Tennessee. In 1949 Mrs. Gaither will publish the interesting *Double Muscadine*, a painstakingly researched historical "whodunit" set in pre-Civil War Mississippi.

Ralph Waldo Emerson, engraving from a drawing by Samuel W. Rowse, ca. 1878. Prints and Photographs Division.

MAY
22

MAY
23

1969 At the opening of its exhibition commemorating the 150th anniversary of the poet's birth, the Library of Congress announces that it will acquire the Charles Feinberg collection of Walt Whitman materials, which includes over 20,000 items.

1803 Ralph Waldo Emerson is born in Boston. "[T]he poet's habit of living should be set on a key so low that the common influences should delight him. His cheerfulness should be the gift of sunlight; the air should suffice for his inspiration, and he should be tipsy with water."

MAY
24

1912 Editor and essayist Norman Cousins is born in Union, New Jersey.

MAY

25

MAY

26

1894 Dashiell Hammett, author of *The Maltese Falcon*, creator of *The Thin Man*, is born in St. Mary's County, Maryland.

1907 Rachel L. Carson, author of the potent environmental warning *Silent Spring*, is born in Springdale, Pennsylvania. "Over increasingly large areas of the United States, spring now comes unheralded by the return of the birds, and the early mornings are strangely silent where once they were filled with the beauty of bird song."

1915 Herman Wouk, author of *The Caine Mutiny Court-Martial* and *War and Remembrance*, is born in New York City.

MAY

27

MAY

28

1916 Walker Percy, author of *The Moviegoer*, born in Birmingham, Alabama.

MAY
29

MAY
30

1901 Author and actres Cornelia Otis Skinner, whc wrote *The Pleasure of Hi Company*, several col lections of humorous es says, and, with Emily Kim brough, the best-sellin memoir *Our Hearts Wer Young and Gay*, is born i Chicago.

1903 African-America poet Countee Cullen– author of *Color, The Blac Christ and Other Poems* and *My Lives and How Lost Them*—is born in Ne York City.

MAY
31

1819 Walt Whitman is born on Long Island, New York.

" Long enough have you dream'd contemptible dreams,
Now I wash the gum from your eyes,
You must habit yourself to the dazzle of the light and of every moment of your life. "

1895 William Allen White buys the Emporia, Kansas, *Gazette* and begins a brilliant career as journalist and commentator. 'Put fear out of your heart. This nation will survive, this state will prosper, the orderly business of life will go forward if only men can speak in whatever way given them to utter what their hearts hold—by voice, by posted card, by letter, or by press. Reason never has failed men. Only force and oppression have made the wrecks in the world.''

1887 Orrick Johns, poet and author of *Time of Our Lives,* is born in St. Louis, Missouri.

1926 Poet Allen Ginsberg is born in Newark, New Jersey.

1917 Robert Anderson, playwright *(Tea and Sympathy),* novelist, and screenwriter, is born in New York City.

1917 The first Pulitzer Prizes are awarded.

JUNE 5

1851 The first installment of *Uncle Tom's Cabin* is published in the Abolitionist journal *The National Era*. "I suffer exquisitely in writing these things," Harriet Beecher Stowe said in a letter. "It may be truly said that I write with my heart's blood. Many times in writing 'Uncle Tom's Cabin' I thought my health would fail utterly; but I prayed earnestly that God would help me till I got through, and still am pressed beyond measure and above strength."

JUNE 6

1892 Writer and illustrator of Western stories Will James, author of *Smoky*, is born in Montana. "It was in 1923, I was not making ends meet, my saddle was still in hock. A friend got after me to try my hand at writing with my drawing. I laughed at him but he was serious, and finally I made him a bet of five dollars that any writing of mine would be returned faster than I could send it. The result was my first article, 'Bucking Horses and Bucking Horse Riders,' in *Scribner's*. The next four following was accepted straight hand running, and then I figured I sure enough was a writer."

1944 D-Day. War correspondent Martha Gellhorn crosses the English Channel on a hospital ship and manages to get ashore to cover the action before returning to London. Meanwhile, her husband, Ernest Hemingway, observes the invasion at Omaha Beach from the deck of a landing craft.

JUNE 7

1917 Poet Gwendolyn Brooks, Library of Congress Consultant in Poetry 1985–86, is born in Topeka, Kansas.

‘ ‘ Build now your church, my brothers, sisters. Build never with brick nor Corten nor with granite. Build with lithe love. With love like lion-eyes. With love like morningrise. With love like black, our black— luminously indiscreet; complete; continuous. ’ ’

JUNE 8

Harriet Beecher Stowe from an engraving in Century magazine, October 1887 (opposite). Prints and Photographs Division

MAGNET LIBRARY NO. 481

The Downward Path

BY

Dick Stewart

STREET & SMITH · PUBLISHERS · NEW YORK

1860 Irwin P. Beadle and his brother Erastus publish the first dime novel, *Maleska: The Indian Wife of the White Hunter* by Ann Sophia Stephens. The book sells 300,000 copies in a year and is followed by hundreds of dime novels about frontiersmen, Indians, train robbers, and chaste heroines.

1893 Playwright Samuel Nathaniel Behrman, author of *No Time for Comedy*, is born in Worcester, Massachusetts.

1928 Artist and author of children's books Maurice Sendak is born in Brooklyn, New York.

1925 William Styron, author of *The Confessions of Nat Turner* and *Sophie's Choice*, is born in Newport News, Virginia.

1894 Poet and teacher of poets Mark Van Doren is born in Hope, Illinois.

One of the nearly 40,000 titles in the dime novel collection, Rare Book and Special Collections Division (opposite).

JUNE
13

JUNE
14

1811 Harriet Beecher Stowe is born in Litchfield, Connecticut.

JUNE
15

JUNE
16

1938 Joyce Carol Oates is born in Lockport, New York.

1880 Critic and novelist Carl Van Vechten is born in Cedar Rapids, Iowa.

1914 John Hersey, author of *A Bell for Adano* and *Hiroshima*, is born in Tientsin, China.

1896 Playwright Philip Barry, whose principal works include *Holiday* and *The Philadelphia Story*, is born in Rochester, New York.

1937 Novelist Gail Godwin is born in Birmingham, Alabama.

1900 Novelist Laura Keane Hobson, author of *Gentleman's Agreement*, is born in New York City.

Lillian Hellman. Prints and Photographs Division.

1865 Walt Whitman is fired from his job as a clerk in the U.S. Department of the Interior, apparently because some critics have called *Leaves of Grass* a dirty book.

1905 Playwright, memoirist, and screenwriter Lillian Hellman is born in New Orleans.

JUNE 21

1912 Novelist and short story writer Mary McCarthy, whose works will be praised for their "acute wit and the malice to propel it," is born in Seattle, Washington. "I taught for a short time at Bard College and at Sarah Lawrence. This awakened me, slowly, to the fact that cleverness is not a substitute for knowledge—a discovery which belatedly, sometimes happily, sometimes uncomfortably, is altering the course of my life."

JUNE 22

1846 Novelist Julian Hawthorne, only son of Nathaniel Hawthorne, is born in Boston. A writer of sensational, sometimes fantastic works, Hawthorne also developed a new variant of the detective story.

1906 Anne Morrow Lindbergh, author of *Gift from the Sea*, is born in Englewood, New Jersey.

JUNE 23

1876 Irvin Shrewsbury Cobb—humorist and author of over 60 books, including *Prose and Cons, Judge Priest Turns Detective*, and *Exit Laughing*—is born in Paducah, Kentucky. Cobb, whose humor will be characterized as "American, in the best tradition of Bill Nye, Artemus Ward, Mark Twain, and Will Rogers," will operate under the following philosophy: "You have to be able to poke fun at yourself before you can poke fun at anyone else without hurting his feelings."

JUNE 24

1842 Ambrose Bierce is born in Meigs County, Ohio.

1916 Poet John Ciardi is born in Boston.

G. B. Shaw with Albert Einstein, by Oliver Herford (opposite). Cabinet of American Illustration, Prints and Photographs Division.

JUNE
25

JUNE
26

1892 Pearl S. Buck, winner of the 1938 Nobel Prize for Literature, is born in Hillsboro, West Virginia. The daughter of missionaries, she will spend her youth in China. "My mother taught me and fitted me for college and gave me all that I have. Most of all did she teach me the beauty that lies in words and in what words will say."

1918 Laurence Stallings is wounded while leading his men in a grenade attack on a machine gun nest on the last day of battle at Belleau Wood, France. He will be awarded the Croix de Guerre and a Silver Star, and will lose his leg as a result of his wound. Stallings will later write a novel and a number of short stories about his war experiences—and, with Maxwell Anderson, the powerful antiwar play *What Price Glory?*

JUNE
27

1850 Peripatetic author and translator Lafcadio Hearn is born in the Greek islands. A writer noted for his sensitivity in the use of language and the exotic moods he could create with words, Hearn will first be published in the United States. Toward the end of his life he will become a citizen of Japan.

JUNE
28

*936 Gone with the
ind, Margaret Mitchell's
nly novel, is published by
acmillan.

rom McGuffey's Third
*lectic Reader, 1879. Gen-
l collections.

JULY 1

1892 Novelist James M. Cain—author of *The Postman Always Rings Twice, Double Indemnity*, and *Mildred Pierce*—is born in Annapolis, Maryland..

1915 Novelist and shor story writer Jean Stafford i born in Covina, California

James M. Cain, from his papers in the Manuscript Division. Photo by Melbourne Spurr.

JULY 2

1961 Ernest Hemingwa dies at age 62 of a sel inflicted gunshot wound i Ketchum, Idaho.

Ernest Hemingway re covering from shrapne wounds, 1919 (opposite Prints and Photograph Division.

JULY 3

JULY 4

1804 Nathaniel Hawthorne, author of *The Scarlet Letter* and the person often credited with establishing the American short story as an art form, is born in Salem, Massachusetts.

1845 Henry David Thoreau begins his sojourn at Walden Pond.

1855 Walt Whitman publishes *Leaves of Grass*.

1895 The poem "Ame ica the Beautiful," by Kat erine Lee Bates, a Wellesle College professor, is fir published in the *Congrega tionalist*.

1916 Poet Alan Seege 28, author of "I Have Rendezvous with Death is killed by German ma chine gun fire at Belloy e Santerre, France.

1927 Playwright Ne Simon is born in New Yo City.

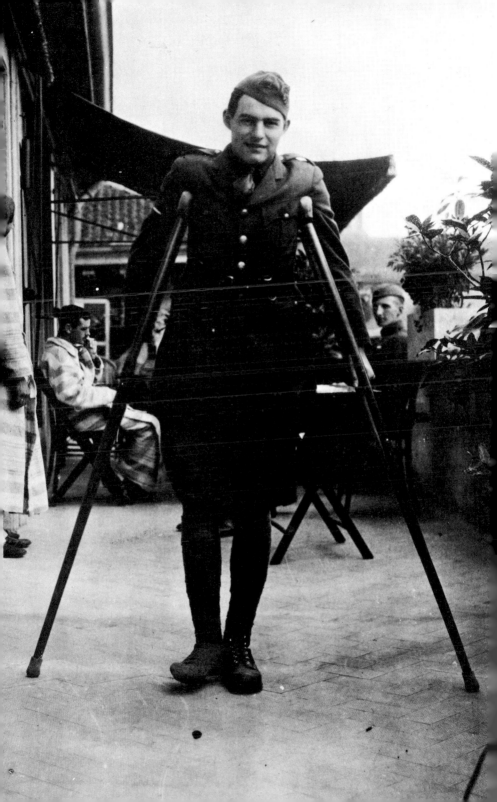

JULY
5

1890 Historian and editor Frederick Lewis Allen—author of *Only Yesterday*, an informal history of the United States—is born in Boston.

JULY
6

1776 The Declaration of Independence is published for the first time in the *Pennsylvania Evening Post* under the title "A Declaration by the Representatives of the United States, in General Congress assembled."

JULY
7

1757 Benjamin Franklin publishes *Poor Richard Improved, Being an Almanac &c. for the year of Our Lord, 1758*. "Sloth, like Rust, consumes faster than Labor wears; while the used key is always bright, as Poor RICHARD says. But dost thou love life? Then do not squander time! for that's the stuff Life is made of, as Poor RICHARD says."

1907 Science fiction writer Robert Heinlein, author of *Stranger in a Strange Land*, is born in Butler, Missouri.

JULY
8

1918 Ernest Hemingway, serving as an American Red Cross ambulance driver in Italy, is wounded in both legs by shrapnel. Despite his wounds, he carries another man to safety. Hemingway's novel *A Farewell to Arms* will reflect this wartime experience.

1887 Pulitzer Prize-winning historian Samuel Eliot Morison, author of *The Oxford History of the American People*, is born in Boston. "A few hints as to literary craftsmanship may be useful to budding historians. First and foremost, *get writing!*"

1894 Journalist Dorothy Thompson, author of the syndicated column *On the Road* and, from 1928 to 1942, wife of Sinclair Lewis, is born in Lancaster, New York.

1834 James Abbott McNeill Whistler, painter and author of *The Gentle Art of Making Enemies*, is born in Lowell, Massachusetts.

1867 Finley Peter Dunne, who, as "Mr. Dooley," was a satirist of such insight and power that he was regarded as America's greatest humorist after Mark Twain, is born in Chicago.

1915 Saul Bellow, who will win the 1976 Nobel Prize for Literature, is born in Lachine, Quebec.

*S*aul Bellow at the Library of Congress, January 1963.

1899 Essayist and children's novelist E. B. White, weaver of *Charlotte's Web*, is born in Mount Vernon, New York. "It was the best place to be, thought Wilbur, this warm delicious cellar, with the garrulous geese, the changing seasons, the heat of the sun, the passage of swallows, the nearness of rats, the sameness of sheep, the love of spiders, the smell of manure, and the glory of everything."

1881 Novelist and short story writer Clarence Budington Kelland—among whose many works is the story upon which the popular movie *Mr. Deeds Goes to Town* is based—is born in Portland, Michigan.

1817 Henry David Thoreau is born in Concord, Massachusetts. "A true account of the actual is the rarest poetry, for common sense always takes a hasty and superficial view."

JULY
13

First edition cover of Owen Wister's The Virginian, *1902. Rare Book and Special Collections Division.*

JULY
14

1642 Benjamin Thompson, the first native American to publish a book of poems in America, is born in Quincy, Massachusetts.

1860 Owen Wister—author of *The Virginian*, in which is coined the immortal phrase "When you call me that, *smile!*"—is born in Philadelphia.

1903 Novelist and biographer Irving Stone, author of *Lust for Life*, is born in San Francisco. "I had always been a hopeless bookworm; from the age of six I had known that I wanted to become a writer. At the age of twenty-three, after having written short stories and one-act plays for several years, I quit the teaching profession altogether and jumped with both hands and feet into the writing game."

1904 Issac Bashevis Singer, who will be awarded the 1978 Nobel Prize for Literature, is born in Radzymin, Poland.

JULY
15

1903 Novelist Walter Dumaux Edmonds, author of *Drums Along the Mohawk* and *Chad Hanna*, is born in Boonville, New York. "The life in our neighborhood, its origins and history, are what have interested me since I started writing in college. I was lucky to be born in New York State, which is almost in miniature a cross-section of the entire United States. All my books and stories have been about New York and there is plenty more for me to write about and for a whole flock of writers too."

Owen Wister, 1893. Prints and Photographs Division.

JULY
16

1889   Erle Stanley
Gardner, creator of Perry
Mason, is born in Malden,
Massachusetts.

1906   Playwright
Clifford Odets, author of
Awake and Sing, *The
Country Girl*, and *Waiting
for Lefty*, is born in Phila-
delphia.

1885 Novelist Mary
O'Hara—whose books *My
Friend Flicka*, *Thunder-
head*, and *Green Grass of
Wyoming* will be translated
into all modern languages
and read all over the world
—is born in New Jersey.

JULY
21

1899 Ernest Hemingway is born in Oak Park, Illinois. "All good books are alike in that they are truer than if they had really happened and after you are finished reading one you will feel that all that happened to you and afterwards it all belongs to you the good and the bad, the ecstasy, the remorse and sorrow, the people and the places and how the weather was. If you can get so that you can give that to people, then you are a writer."

1899 Poet Hart Crane is born in Garrettsville, Ohio

1933 Novelist John Gardner is born in Batavia, New York.

Nathaniel Hawthorne, from an 1840 painting by Charles Osgood (opposite) Prints and Photograph Division.

JULY
22

'' American Muse, whose strong and diverse heart
So many men have tried to understand
But only made it smaller with their art
Because you are as various as your land. ''

1898 Poet Stephen Vincent Benet, author of "John Brown's Body," is born in Bethlehem, Pennsylvania.

JULY
23

1880 Mystery writer Raymond Chandler, author of *Farewell, My Lovely, The Big Sleep*, and *The Long Goodbye*, is born in Chicago. "Often, I suppose I've been asked why, with my sort of background, I wrote the kind of lowlife fiction I did. . . .[T]his elaborate overtooled civilization of ours just strikes me that way. The story of our time to me is not war nor atomic energy but the marriage of an idealist to a gangster and how their home life and children turned out."

JULY
24

1916 John D. MacDonald, creator of Travis McGee, is born in Sharon, Pennsylvania. "I would not demand that a man read ponderous tomes, or try to read everything. . . . I would expect that in his reading—which should be wide ranging fiction, history, poetry, political science—he would acquire the equivalent of liberal arts education and acquire also what I think of as the educated climate of mind, a climate characterized by skepticism, irony, doubt, hope, and a passion to learn more and remember more."

1856 Historical novelist Charles Major, author of *When Knighthood Was in Flower*, is born in Indianapolis, Indiana.

1866 George Barr McCutcheon—writer of romantic fiction and author of *Brewster's Millions* —is born on a farm near Lafayette, Indiana. Though he sometimes longed to be taken more seriously as a writer, McCutcheon may have expressed his basic philosophy when he said, "Why read for realism when one can read for thrills?"

1897 Sportswriter, short story writer, and screenwriter Paul William Gallico, author of *The Snow Goose*, is born in New York City. "Five hours a day total is the most I can write. Often when I get stuck I talk to myself on the typewriter. The mechanical effort of doing this usually bypasses the mental block and ideas flow again."

1869 Booth Tarkington, author of *The Magnificent Ambersons*, *Penrod*, and *Alice Adams*, is born in Indianapolis, Indiana. As a novelist, Tarkington's chief concern was "the truth and mystery of human nature." From *Penrod*: "They were upon their great theme: 'When I get to be a man!' Being human, though boys, they considered their present estate too commonplace to be dwelt upon. So, when the old men gather, they say: 'When I was a boy!' It really is the land of nowadays that we never discover."

1878 Don Marquis—novelist, poet, dramatist, and creator of *archy* (the typing cockroach) *and mehitabel* (the cat)—is born in Walnut, Illinois. "i have noticed that when chickens quit quarreling over their food they often find that there is enough for all of them i wonder if it might not be the same with the human race." (a random thought by archy)

Illustration by George Herriman from The Lives and Times of Archy and Mehitabel *by Don Marquis, 1950.*

1918 Novelist Edwin O'Connor, author of *The Last Hurrah*, is born in Providence, Rhode Island.

1857 Ironical social scientist and writer of "desperately accurate circumlocutions" Thorstein Veblen, author of *The Theory of the Leisure Class*, is born in Cato, Wisconsin.

1918 Poet Joyce Kilmer, 31, author of "Trees," is killed in France while serving with the 165th Infantry near Seringes on the Western Front. He is awarded the Croix de Guerre, posthumously.

1815 Richard Henry Dana, Jr., author of *Two Years Before the Mast*, is born in Cambridge, Massachusetts.

1819 Herman Melville is born in New York City. "Say what some poets will, Nature is not so much her own ever-sweet interpreter, as the mere supplier of that cunning alphabet, whereby selecting and combining as he pleases, each man reads his own peculiar lesson according to his own peculiar mind and mood."

AUGUST

1

AUGUST

2

1924 James Baldwin, author of *The Fire Next Time*, is born in New York City.

Ernie Pyle, May 1945. Prints and Photographs Division.

1900 Journalist Ernie Pyle is born on a farm near Dana, Indiana.

1909 Novelist and short story writer Walter Van Tilburg Clark, author of *The Ox-Bow Incident*, is born in East Orlando, Maine.

1924 Leon Uris, author of *Exodus* and *Trinity*, is born in Baltimore.

AUGUST

3

AUGUST

4

1913 Novelist, short story writer, and playwright Jerome Weidman, whose most celebrated work is *I Can Get It for You Wholesale*, is born in New York City.

AUGUST
5

1889 Poet, novelist, and short story writer Conrad Aiken is born in Savannah, Georgia. Aiken's career included many awards and distinctions—including serving as Library of Congress Consultant in Poetry, 1950–51. But perhaps the most unusual distinction resulted from his refusal to serve in the armed forces during World War I on the grounds that as a poet he was engaged in an "essential industry": He is the first American poet to be excused from war duty in order to write poetry.

AUGUST
6

AUGUST
7

1945 U.S. Army Air Corps second lieutenant Mac Hyman, who will later write *No Time for Sergeants*, takes the first photographs of devastated Hiroshima, on which the atomic bomb had been dropped the day before from a B-29 reconnaissance plane.

1884 Poet Sara Teasdale is born in St. Louis, Missouri.

1896 Marjorie Kinnan Rawlings, author of *The Yearling* and *Cross Creek* is born in Washington, DC. "I have no free swing in what I write, no little miracles. I let my novels mature for several years, know almost exactly what I want to do in them, and slowly do it."

AUGUST
8

Title page, Davy Crockett's Almanack, *1838 (opposite) Rare Book and Special Collections Division.*

Davy Crockett's
18 ALMANACK, 38
OF WILD SPORTS IN THE WEST,
Life in the Backwoods, Sketches of Texas, and Rows on the Mississippi.

Nashville, Tennessee.   Published by the heirs of Col. Crockett.

AUGUST
9

AUGUST
10

1881 Poet, playwright and translator Witter Byn ner is born in Brooklyn New York.

AUGUST
11

1897 Louise Bogan poet, critic, and Library o Congress Consultant i Poetry 1945–46, is born i Livermore Falls, Maine.

1921 Alex Haley, autho of *Roots* and *The Autobiog raphy of Malcolm X*, i born in Ithaca, New York

---

AUGUST
12

1905 An appreciation of the poetry of Edwin Arlington Robinson written by President Theodore Roose-velt is published in *Ou look*. A writer himsel Roosevelt had become a admirer of Robinson' work after reading *Th Children of the Night* i 1904. In 1905 Roosevel provided the poverty stricken Robinson with government job—"speci agent of the Treasury" i the Customs House on Wa Street—that enabled th poet to spend a minimu of time in the office and maximum amount of tim writing.

1834 Richard Henry Dana, Jr., sails as a common seaman aboard the *Pilgrim*, beginning the adventures he would later record in *Two Years Before the Mast*.

1925 Journalist, essayist, and memoirist Russell Baker is born in Loudoun County, Virginia.

1887 Novelist and playwright Edna Ferber, author of *Show Boat*, *So Big*, and *Cimarron*, is born in Kalamazoo, Michigan.

1944 During novelist Joseph Heller's 37th mission as a wing bombardier in a B-25 bomber, a gunner wounded, "a co-pilot went a little berserk at the controls and I came to the startling realization—Good God! They're trying to kill me too!" This experience finds its way into Heller's first novel, *Catch-22*.

"*Life's Fundamental Museum*" by *Oliver Herford*. Cabinet of American Illustration, Prints and Photographs Division.

Illustration by Robert McCloskey from his Homer Price, 1943 (opposite). General collections.

AUGUST

17

AUGUST

18

" There is only one way to achieve happiness on this terrestrial ball, And that is to have either a clear conscience, or none at all. "

AUGUST

19

1902 Humorist-poe Ogden Nash, author o many keen, inventivel rhymed observations, i born in Rye, New York.

1903 Novelist Jame Gould Cozzens, whos *Guard of Honor* wa awarded the Pulitzer Priz in 1948, is born in Chicage

1914 On Trial, the fir play by Elmer Rice, oper in New York City and ir troduces the dramatic de vice of the flashback.

AUGUST

20

1890 Fantasist and ho ror story writer Howar Phillips Lovecraft *(Th Dunwich Horror)* is bor in Providence, Rhod Island. A literary disciple Edgar Allan Poe, Lovecra felt so much more at hom writing during the da hours that he would dra the curtains and work b electric light even durir the day.

PRICE 5 CENTS

OLD SLEUTH WEEKLY

No. 126

Price 5 cents

PRESTO QUICK

by "OLD SLEUTH"

THE
WESTBROOK

An early detective serial in the Rare Book and Special Collections Division (opposite).

AUGUST
21

1893 Satirical author and poet Dorothy Parker—once described by Alexander Woollcott as "so odd a blend of Little Nell and Lady Macbeth"—is born in West End, New Jersey. "Wit has truth in it; wisecracking is simply calisthenics with words."

1920 Playwright, poet, and science fiction writer Ray Bradbury, author of *The Martian Chronicles*, is born in Waukegan, Illinois.

AUGUST
22

1869 Poet, novelist, and biographer Edgar Lee Masters, author of *Spoon River Anthology*, is born in Garnett, Kansas.

1884 Humorist Will (William Jacob) Cuppy is born in Auburn, Indiana. Cuppy was the author of such helpful and informative tomes as *How to Be a Hermit, How to Tell Your Friends from the Apes*, and *The Decline and Fall of Practically Everybody*.

1917 John Dos Passos writes a friend from the Western Front, where he is serving as an ambulance driver: "The war is utter damn nonsense—a vast cancer fed by lies and self seeking malignity on the part of those who don't do the fighting." Dos Passos's World War I experience will form the basis for his first novel, *One Man's Invitation-1917*.

AUGUST
23

AUGUST
24

1898 Critic and editor Malcolm Cowley, author of *Exile's Return* and *The Literary Situation*, is born in Belsano, Pennsylvania.

AUGUST
25

1836 Bret Harte, author of *The Luck of Roaring Camp* and *The Outcasts of Poker Flat*, is born in Albany, New York.

1944 Leading a group of French resistance fighters, Ernest Hemingway ''liberates'' the bar at the Hotel Ritz in Paris.

AUGUST
26

1871 Theodore Dreiser is born in Terre Haute, Indiana. Founder of a new school of realism in American fiction, Dreiser found it necessary to engage in a long battle against censorship and for the right of the serious novelist to present life as he sees it when his own first novel, *Sister Carrie*, was withdrawn from circulation immediately after its publication because of objections to its content.

1874 Novelist, short story writer, dramatist, and poet Zona Gale—whose Pulitzer Prize-winning novel *Miss Lulu Bett* will be ranked with the work of Sinclair Lewis and Theodore Dreiser—is born in Portage, Wisconsin.

1884 Earl Derr Biggers —playwright, novelist, and creator of detective Charlie Chan—is born in Ohio.

Theodore Dreiser by Co varrubias. Prints and Pho tographs Division.

AUGUST
27

AUGUST
28

1813 Reclusive mystical poet Jones Very, a protégé of Ralph Waldo Emerson, is born in Salem, Massachusetts.

1908 Nature writer Roger Tory Peterson is born in Jamestown, New York.

Henry David Thoreau, 1879. Prints and Photographs Division.

Oliver Wendell Holmes. Prints and Photographs Division.

AUGUST
29

1809 Oliver Wendell Holmes, author of "Old Ironsides" and *The Autocrat at the Breakfast Table*, is born in Cambridge, Massachusetts. "I find the great thing in this world is not so much where we stand, as in what direction we are moving."

1837 Henry David Thoreau startles a Harvard commencement audience, which he is addressing on the topic "The Commercial Spirit of Modern Times," by condemning that spirit as "a blind and unmanly love of wealth." "The order of things should be somewhat reversed; the seventh should be man's day of toil, wherein to earn his living by the sweat of his brow; and the other six his Sabbath of the affections and the soul—in which to range his wide-spread garden, and drink in the soft influences and sublime revelations of nature."

1901 Journalist and author John Gunther, author of *Inside Europe* and *Death Be Not Proud*, is born in Chicago.

AUGUST
30

1837 Ralph Waldo Emerson delivers his celebrated *American Scholar* address—dubbed "America's Declaration of Intellectual Independence" by Oliver Wendell Holmes—before the Phi Beta Kappa Society at Harvard. "Our day of dependence, our long apprenticeship to the learning of other lands, is drawing to a close. The millions that around us are rushing into life, cannot always be fed on the sere remains of foreign harvests."

1885 Novelist and dramatist DuBose Heyward—author of the novel *Porgy*, which later became the Gershwin opera *Porgy and Bess*—is born in Charleston, South Carolina.

1908 Story writer and playwright William Saroyan is born in Fresno, California. The author of *The Human Comedy* and the Pulitzer Prize-winning *The Time of Your Life* was not known for his humility: "I am so innately great that by comparison others who believe they are great or act as if they believe they are great seem to me to be only pathetic, although occasionally charming."

AUGUST
31

SEPTEMBER
1

1875 Edgar Rice Burroughs, creator of Tarzan, is born in Chicago.

1888 Clement Wood, poet and author of *Hunters of Heaven*, a discourse on American poetry, and *The Complete Rhyming Dictionary and Poet's Craft Book*, is born in Tuscaloosa, Alabama.

Illustration by J. Allen St. John for a 1934 entry in the wildly popular Tarzan series. General collections.

SEPTEMBER
2

1917 Social historian and novelist Cleveland Amory is born in Nahant, Massachusetts.

SEPTEMBER
3

1849 Sarah Orne Jewett—a writer whose work was drawn from and revelatory of New England life—is born in South Berwick, Maine.

1926 Novelist Alison Lurie, author of *The War Between the Tates*, is born in Chicago.

*Richard Wright, 1943.
Photo by Gordon Parks.
Prints and Photographs
Division.*

1908 Richard Wright, who wrote *Black Boy* and *American Hunger*, is born on a plantation near Natchez, Mississippi.

1859 Probably the first novel by a black author to appear in the U.S., *Our Nig; or Sketches from the Life of a Free Black* by Harriet E. Whilson, is issued in Boston by the firm of George C. Rand and Avery. Little is known about the author save that she published the autobiographical work to raise funds for the care of her son. The novel was rediscovered and republished in 1983.

1916 Frank Yerby, author of *The Foxes of Harrow*, is born in Augusta, Georgia. "The novelist hasn't any right to inflict on the public his private ideas on politics, religion or race. If he wants to preach he should go on the pulpit."

' I was, being human, born alone;
I am, being woman, hard beset,
I live by squeezing from a stone
The little nourishment I get. '
—Elinor Wylie

1885 Poet and novelist Elinor Wylie, author of *Nets to Catch the Wind*, is born in Somerville, New Jersey.

1900 Anglo-American novelist Taylor Caldwell, author of *Dear and Glorious Physician*, is born near Manchester, Lancashire, England.

1903 Margaret Dorothea Landon, author of the bestselling *Anna and the King of Siam* (later made into the hit musical *The King and I*), is born in Somers, Wisconsin. In doing research on this story of the relationship between Siamese King Mongkut and Mrs. Anna Leonowens, Ms. Landon discovered the king's letters, published in Siamese, in the collections of the Library of Congress.

SEPTEMBER
8

1947 Novelist and short story writer Ann Beattie is born in Washington, DC.

SEPTEMBER
9

SEPTEMBER
10

1885 Editor, critic, and biographer Carl Van Doren, who helped give the study of American literature a systematic place in university curricula and wrote widely on literary and historical subjects, is born in Hope, Illinois.

1886 Poet Hilda Doolittle (H. D.) is born in Bethlehem, Pennsylvania.

1862 William Sydney Porter—who as O. Henry was master of short stories with a twist—is born in Greensboro, North Carolina.

SEPTEMBER
11

The Jig-Saw Murder Case *by Robert Wallace, a 1933 whodunit in which the reader literally pieces together the solution (opposite). Rare Book and Special Collections Division.*

down. Powerful fingers were at his throat—attempting to strangle him. Behind him, in the sudden darkness, Trimm, too, was struggling with an assailant. Neither could be of aid to the other. Those great strangling hands worked relentlessly at his throat. Two awful thumbs dug into his windpipe. This must be the *strangler*—the murderer of the girl in the library, the mad killer of Silo Murzin! Could he escape?

Frantically he attempted to dislodge those horrible hands. His strength was leaving him. That hold. He must break it. With his last despairing energy he struck straight into the pit of the man's stomach. For the flash of a second the fingers relaxed their grip. Adams took a deep breath. It was like taking a strong drink. Life was in his muscles again. Now for a jujutsu stroke—if he could put it across. His right hand struck across the tense cords of the man's neck, sidewise like a knife. The powerful brute went down with a thump. Adams recovered his fallen automatic.

As Adams sprang back he became aware of another figure groping about near him. It was Trimm, his assailant satisfactorily disposed of. In a moment Trimm found what he sought. The revealing beam of his flashlight stabbed through the darkness, centering on the district attorney and his captive. Adams gazed down into the blinking eyes of his antagonist—the heavy-set, red-faced man he had once seen on the street with Jib Bacon, the *Journal* reporter. He jabbed his automatic against the man's ribs.

"Who are you?" he demanded.

NOW GO ON WITH THE STORY . . .

Fit together the intricate details that lead to the solution of the Jig-saw Puzzle Mystery you have just been reading.

Who is the strangler?

What is the mystery of the girl on the stairway?

Who killed Miriam Kidd Sloane?

What is the real secret of the old Kidd house?

. . . And where is the missing bit of wood that helps to solve *the jig-saw murder?*

The Solution is in the Jig-saw Puzzle sealed under this page.

To open, run your finger-nail along dotted line.

H. L. Mencken. Prints and Photographs Division.

1880 Editor and essayist H. L. (Henry Louis) Mencken, author of *The American Language*, is born in Baltimore.

1728 Mercy Warren, friend of American patriots such as Thomas Jefferson and John Adams, and a writer devoted to the American republic *(History of the Rise, Progress and Termination of the American Revolution)* is born in Barnstable, Massachusetts.

1814 Lawyer Francis Scott Key, on his way to secure the release of an American citizen being held by the British, writes "The Star Spangled Banner" while detained on a British ship throughout the 25-hour bombardment of Ft. McHenry, Baltimore, during the War of 1812. The words will later be set to a British tune, *Anacreon in Heaven*.

1876 Novelist, poet, and short story writer Sherwood Anderson, author of *Winesburg, Ohio*, is born in Camden, Ohio.

1888 Novelist and librarian Frances Newman is born in Atlanta. Her two novels—*The Hard-Boiled Virgin* (banned in Boston!) and *Dead Lovers are Faithful Lovers*—created sensations, not entirely because of the involved, exotic style in which they were written.

Sherwood Anderson by Stieglitz. Prints and Photographs Division.

H. L. Mencken by Covarrubias (opposite). Prints and Photographs Division.

1860 Midwestern novelist and essayist Hamlin Garland, author of *A Son of the Middle Border* and its Pulitzer Prize-winning sequel *A Daughter of the Middle Border*, is born in a log cabin near West Salem, Wisconsin.

SEPTEMBER 15

1889 Humorist Robert Charles Benchley—who will be called "perhaps the most finished master of the technique of literary fun in America"—is born in Worcester, Massachusetts. Among his works: *My Ten Years in a Quandary* and *Benchley Beside Himself.*

1890 Poet and novelist Claude McKay, one of the foremost figures in the so-called "Negro literary renaissance" of the 1920s, is born in Sunny Ville, Jamaica, West Indies.

SEPTEMBER 16

1823 Historian Francis Parkman—who will travel the Oregon Trail, living for a time with a band of Sioux Indians, and then write of his experiences in *The California and Oregon Trail* —is born in Boston. "Faithfulness to the truth of history involves far more than a research, however patient and scrupulous, into special facts. . . . The narrator must seek to imbue himself with the life and spirit of the time. He must study events in the bearings near and remote; in the character, habits, and manners of those who took part in them. He must himself be, as it were, a sharer or a spectator of the action he describes."

1830 Oliver Wendell Holmes writes the poem "Old Ironsides," about the frigate *Constitution,* for the Boston *Daily Advertiser.* The impassioned poem will become so popular that the order for dismantling the ship will be rescinded.

SEPTEMBER 17

1942 Mystery writer Dashiell Hammett reenlists in the U.S. Army (he had served during World War I). He will spend most of his service on Adak, a barren island in the Aleutians, where, among his other duties, he will start a camp newspaper, the *Adakian.*

1883 Poet, novelist, and physician William Carlos Williams is born in Rutherford, New Jersey. "That is the poet's business. Not to talk in vague categories but to write particularly, as a physician works, upon a patient, upon the thing before him, in the particular to discover the universal."

William Randolph Hearst by Oliver Herford. Cabinet of American Illustration, Prints and Photographs Division.

SEPTEMBER 18

1894 Novelist and writer for children Rachel Lyman Field, author of *Time Out of Mind* and *All This and Heaven Too*, is born in New York City.

1878 Upton Sinclair, author of the muckraking novel *The Jungle* about methods and conditions in the Chicago stockyards (a memorable book about which he once said that he aimed at the people's heart —and hit their stomach) is born in Baltimore.

1892 Columnist and humorist Frank Sullivan, creator of "Mr. Arbuthnot" and author of such collections of essays as *The Night Old Nostalgia Burned Down* and *Moose in the Moose*, is born in Saratoga Springs, New York.

1956 Mystery writer Mary Roberts Rinehart, 80 —author of *The Circular Staircase*, *The Yellow Room*, and *The Swimming Pool*—dies. Foul play is not suspected.

It is the time, too, when you and papa tell us so many nice stories as we all sit by the fire in the cold evenings. Don't you like winter, mamma?"

"Yes, my dear; and I like all the seasons, for there is much that is pleasant in each of them. If we do not spend our time in finding fault, but learn to see what is bright and good in all that is around us, we may be happy in any season."

SEPTEMBER

23

1800 Educator William Holmes McGuffey, compiler of the McGuffey Eclectic Readers, is born near Claysville, Pennsylvania. The readers will sell approximately 122 million copies and will be a major influence in shaping the American mind in the mid-19th century.

1896 Francis Scott Key Fitzgerald is born in St. Paul, Minnesota. "All good writing is swimming under water and holding your breath."

SEPTEMBER

24

William Faulkner in the early 1950s. Prints and Photographs Division.

SEPTEMBER

25

1897 William Faulkner, winner of the 1950 Nobel Prize for Literature, is born in New Albany, Mississippi. "[The writer] must teach himself that the basest of all things is to be afraid; and, teaching himself that, forget it forever, leaving no room in his workshop for anything but the old verities and truths of the heart, the old universal truths lacking which any story is ephemeral and doomed— love and honor and pity and pride and compassion and sacrifice."

1898 Drama critic and novelist Richard Lockridge, creator of the breezy and sophisticated detective team of Mr. and Mrs. North, is born in St. Joseph, Missouri.

1905 Sportswriter Red (Walter Wellesley) Smith is born in Green Bay, Wisconsin.

SEPTEMBER
26

1888 T. S. (Thomas Stearns) Eliot, who will be awarded the 1948 Nobel Prize for Literature, is born in St. Louis, Missouri. "As things are, and as fundamentally they must always be, poetry is not a career, but a mug's game. No honest poet can ever feel quite sure of the permanent value of what he has written: he may have wasted his time and messed up his life for nothing."

SEPTEMBER
27

1917 Novelist Louis Auchincloss is born in Lawrence, New York.

SEPTEMBER
28

1892 Playwright Elmer Rice—Pulitzer Prize winner for *Street Scene* and author of *The Adding Machine* and *Dream Girl*—is born in New York City.

SEPTEMBER
29

1924 Truman Capote—author of *Other Voices, Other Rooms, In Cold Blood*, and *A Christmas Memory*—is born in New Orleans. "Though I have always been conscious of style, I have not a 'fixed' style and hope that I never do, for each story requires a new setting of tone, a language that will contain the story as a glass contains water."

1976 In the first major attempt at copyright reform since 1909, Congress approves legislation extending protection for 50 years after the death of an author, artist, or composer and restricting reproduction of copyrighted material.

James Fenimore Cooper, from a painting ca. 1861. Prints and Photographs Division.

OCTOBER
1

1893 Prolific novelist Faith Baldwin—whose works include *Men Are Such Fools!*, *Rich Girl, Poor Girl*, and *Sleeping Beauty* (no, not that one)—is born in New Rochelle, New York.

1885 Poet and anthologist Louis Untermeyer, Library of Congress Consultant in Poetry, 1961–63, is born in New York City.

1914 Historian and Librarian of Congress (1975–87) Daniel J. Boorstin, author of *The American Experience* and *The Discoverers*, is born in Atlanta, Georgia.

OCTOBER
2

1879 Poet Wallace Stevens is born in Reading, Pennsylvania. "Poetry is poetry, and one's objective as a poet is to achieve poetry precisely as one's objective in music is to achieve music."

Thomas Wolfe, artist unknown. Prints and Photographs Division.

OCTOBER
3

1900 Prodigious novelist Thomas Wolfe, author of *Look Homeward, Angel*, is born in Asheville, North Carolina. "If a man has a talent and cannot use it, he has failed. If he has a talent and uses only half of it, he has partly failed. If he has a talent and learns somehow to use the whole of it, he has gloriously succeeded, and won a satisfaction and a triumph few men ever know."

1925 Novelist, playwright, and essayist Gore Vidal is born in West Point, New York.

1862 The amazing Edward L. Stratemeyer—author of over 150 books for children and originator of over 600 more—is born in Elizabeth, New Jersey. A man who will (evidently) come to believe that there cannot be too much of a good thing, he will create under various pseudonyms, the Rover Boys series, the Nancy Drew series, the Tom Swift series, the Hardy Boys series and others.

1884 Journalist, short story writer, and dedicated coffee-drinker (40 cups a day) Damon Runyon is born in Manhattan, Kansas. Once called "the prose laureate of the semi-literate American," the author of "The Idyll of Miss Sarah Brown," which on stage and screen became the immensely successful *Guys and Dolls*, had this to say about his own work: "As a study in the art of carrying water on both shoulders, of sophistry, of writing with tongue-in-cheek, and of intellectual dishonesty, I think it has no superior since the beginning of time."

1915 *Detective Story Magazine*, the first pulp magazine to publish detective fiction exclusively, appears. It will continue to publish for 34 years.

1895 Novelist and critic Caroline Gordon, author of *None Shall Look Back*, *The Strange Children*, and *How to Read a Novel*, is born in Todd County, Kentucky.

1849 Poet, lecturer, and newspaperman James Whitcomb Riley, creator of "Little Orphant Annie," is born in Greenfield, Indiana.

OCTOBER

8

1942 Correspondent (for Time, Inc.) John Hersey accompanies troops during the third Battle of Matani-kau River on Guadalcanal and is later cited by the Secretary of the Navy for helping to remove wounded men from the field under fire. Hersey's first novel, the Pulitzer Prize-winning *A Bell for Adano* will be based on his wartime experiences in Italy a year later.

OCTOBER

9

1922 *R.U.R* (Rossum's Universal Robots), a play by the Czech writer Karel Capek—in which the term *robot* (automaton) is introduced—opens at the Garrick Theatre in New York City.

1899 Journalist and historian Bruce Catton, author of *Mr. Lincoln's Army*, *Glory Road*, and the Pulitzer Prize-winning *A Stillness at Appomattox*, is born in Petoskey, Michigan. "Writing history is the same thing as being a reporter. You try to get the real facts, not the made-up stories. It has the advantage that you don't get talked back to"

OCTOBER

10

1899 The Library of Congress requests funds to purchase an electric automobile to replace the Library's one wagon and two horses.

OCTOBER

11

1759 Mason Locke ("Parson") Weems—from whose biography of

George Washington the myth of the cherry tree grew—is born near Herring Bay, Maryland. " 'George,' said his father, 'do you know who killed that beautiful little cherry tree yonder in the garden?' . . . Looking at his father with the sweet face of youth brightened with the inexpressible charm of all-conquering truth, he bravely cried out. 'I can't tell a lie. I did cut it with my hatchet.' "

1844 Novelist, philanthropist, and reformer George Washington Cable is born in New Orleans. A largely self-educated and most outspoken man, Cable produced a number of books *(Old Creole Days, Strange and True Stories of Louisiana)* praised for their vivacity, Gallic brilliance, and exotic atmosphere. He traveled thousands of miles each year—sometimes accompanying Mark Twain—to give readings from his works.

1890 Historical novelist Conrad Richter, author of *The Sea of Grass, The Town,* and *The Light in the Forest,* is born in Pine Grove, Pennsylvania.

e. e. cummings around 1915. Prints and Photographs Division.

1894 Poet e. e. (Edward Estlin) cummings is born in Cambridge, Massachusetts. "So far as I am concerned, poetry and every other art was and is and forever will be strictly and distinctly a question of individuality . . . If poetry is your goal, you've got to forget all about punishments and all about rewards and all about selfstyled obligations and duties and responsibilities etcetera ad infinitum and remember one thing only: that it's you—nobody else —who determine your destiny and decide your fate."

OCTOBER
15

1830 Poet, novelist, and essayist Helen Hunt Jackson—best known for the novel *Ramona*, which helped foster a more sympathetic attitude among whites toward American Indians—is born in Amherst, Massachusetts.

1917 Historian Arthur M. Schlesinger, Jr.—author of *The Age of Jackson* and *A Thousand Days*, about the Kennedy presidency—is born in Columbus, Ohio.

1920 Novelist Mario *(The Godfather)* Puzo is born in New York City.

OCTOBER
16

1758 Noah Webster is born in West Hartford, Connecticut.

1888 Eugene O'Neill—winner of the 1936 Nobel Prize for Literature and multiple Pulitzer Prizes—is born in New York City.

1898 Travel writer—and Supreme Court Justice—William Orville Douglas, author of *Strange Lands and Friendly People*, is born in Maine, Minnesota.

Eugene O'Neill. Prints and Photographs Division.

OCTOBER
17

1915 Playwright Arthur Miller—author of *Death of a Salesman*, *The Crucible*, and *All My Sons*—is born in New York City. "A book that changed my life was *The Brothers Karamazov*, which I picked up, I don't know how or why, and all at once believed I was born to be a writer."

OCTOBER
18

1865 Anglo-American essayist Logan Pearsall Smith is born in Millville, New Jersey. "What I like in a good author is not what he says, but what he whispers."

1889 Novelist and short story writer Fannie Hurst—who will be dubbed "the sobsister of American fiction"—is born in Hamilton, Ohio. Among her books are *Back Street* and *Imitation of Life*.

1896 Harold Lenoir Davis—poet, novelist, and "literary pioneer of the American West"—is born near Yonoalla, Oregon. Among his books are *Beulah Land* and his Pulitzer Prize-winning first novel *Honey in the Horn*.

1906 Playwright Sidney Kingsley, author of *Men in White*, is born in New York City.

OCTOBER
19

OCTOBER
20

F. *Scott Fitzgerald, 1937.*
Photo by Carl van Vechten.
Prints and Photographs
Division.

1859 John Dewey, "the
dean of American philos-
ophers," is born in Burling-
ton, Vermont.

OCTOBER
21

1976 The Nobel Prize
for Literature is awarded to
Saul Bellow "for the hu-
man understanding and
subtle analysis of contemporary culture that are
combined in his work."

OCTOBER
22

1962 Over 30 poets take
part in the Library of Congress's first National Poetry
Festival.

1788 Sara Josepha Hale, author of ''Mary's Lamb'' (whose fleece was white as snow), is born in Newport, New Hampshire.

1904 Playwright Moss Hart—who collaborated with George S. Kaufman on many plays and wrote the diverting autobiography *Act One*—is born in New York City.

1866 Gilbert Patten, writer of boys' books under the pseudonym ''Burt L. Standish,'' is born in Corinna, Maine. In 1896 Patten created the popular, virtuous, and athletic hero Frank Merriwell, a Yale man, whose exploits were recounted in 208 dime novels that sold 125 million copies.

1902 Historian Henry Steele Commager is born in Pittsburgh.

1941 Novelist Anne Tyler, author of *The Accidental Tourist*, *Celestial Navigation*, and *Morgan's Passing*, is born in Minneapolis.

1917 F. Scott Fitzgerald is commissioned a second lieutenant in the U.S. Infantry and in November reports for training at Fort Leavenworth, Kansas, where the captain in charge of his platoon is Dwight D. Eisenhower.

OCTOBER
27

1787   The first of 77 essays explaining the new U.S. Constitution and urging ratification appears in a New York newspaper. The essays, written by Alexander Hamilton, James Madison, and John Jay, are later published collectively as *The Federalist Papers.*

OCTOBER
28

OCTOBER
29

1921 Cartoonist and author Bill (William Henry) Mauldin is born in Mountain Park, New Mexico.

OCTOBER
30

1885 Ezra Pound is born in Harley, Idaho.

Susan B. Anthony, ca. 1904. Prints and Photographs Division.

NOVEMBER

1

1871 Poet and novelist Stephen Crane, author of *Maggie: A Girl of the Streets* and *The Red Badge of Courage*, is born in Newark, New Jersey.

NOVEMBER

2

NOVEMBER

3

1794 Poet, critic, newspaper editor, lawyer, and defender of human rights William Cullen Bryant—author of "Thanatopsis" and "To a Waterfowl"—is born in Cummington, Massachusetts.

NOVEMBER

4

1897 Good-humored humorist Will ("I never met a man I didn't like") Rogers is born near Oolagah, Indian Territory (Oklahoma).

1885 Will (William James) Durant—author of *The Story of Philosophy* and the vividly written, multivolume "Story of Civilization"—is born in North Adams, Massachusetts. "I am a lover of the lovers of wisdom. I am an historian who loves philosophy."

1943 Playwright and actor Sam Shepard (Samuel Shepard Rogers) is born in Ft. Sheridan, Illinois.

1921 James Jones, author of *From Here to Eternity*, is born in Robinson, Illinois. "There is no especial reason why I should have become a writer. I did not come of a particularly literary family. I was stationed at Hickam Field in Hawaii when I stumbled upon the works of Thomas Wolfe, and his home life seemed so similar to my own, his feelings about himself so similar to mine about myself, that I realized I had been a writer all my life without knowing it or having written. Once I made up my mind, it seemed inevitable, something that fate had directed ever since my birth."

1731 Frontier captain, memoirist, and dramatist Robert Rogers, leader of Rogers's Rangers, whose exploits will make them famous in pre-Revolutionary America, is born in Methuen, Massachusetts. Rogers's 1766 play about Pontiac's Conspiracy, *Ponteach*, is the first tragedy written on a Native American subject.

Paul Laurence Dunbar, frontispiece from Lyrics of Sunshine and Shadow, 1905. General collections.

1897 At the Library of Congress, a reading room for the blind is opened and a special program of readings is inaugurated. One of the first programs features poet Paul Laurence Dunbar, a Library staff member, who reads from his works.

1900 Margaret Mitchell, whose only book was the phenomenal *Gone with the Wind* (submitted to her publisher under the title "Tomorrow Is Another Day" and its heroine named "Pansy"), is born in Atlanta, Georgia.

1928 Poet Anne Sexton is born in Newton, Massachusetts.

Vachel Lindsay. Prints and Photographs Division.

1879 Vachel Lindsay, author of the rhythmic poem "The Congo," is born in Springfield, Illinois.

1893 John Phillips Marquand—author of the Pulitzer Prize-winning novel *The Late George Apley* and the Mr. Moto detective stories *(Thank You, Mr. Moto, Think Fast, Mr. Moto, Mr. Moto Is So Sorry)*—is born in Wilmington, Delaware.

1846 Anna Katherine Green, creator of detective Ebenezer Gryce and sometimes called the "godmother" of detective fiction, is born in Brooklyn, New York.

1922 Kurt Vonnegut is born in Indianapolis.

1815 Elizabeth Cady Stanton, writer, lecturer, a leader of the 19th-century woman-suffrage movement and author of *Eighty Years and More*, is born in Johnstown, New York.

1890 The first volume of Emily Dickinson's poetry is published, posthumously. Many of the poems had been discovered by the poet's sister, Lavinia, stitched together and placed in a camphorwood chest in the poet's room.

1861 Historian Frederick Jackson Turner, author of the epoch-making *The Frontier in American History*, is born in Portage, Wisconsin.

1851 **Thar she blows!** *Moby Dick* is published by Harper & Brothers in New York.

M*arianne Moore at the Library of Congress for a reading of her poems, October 1963.*

1887 Poet and Yankee fan Marianne Moore is born in St. Louis, Missouri. "What Miss Moore's best poetry does," fellow poet Randall Jarrell will write, "I can say best in her own words: it comes into and steadies the soul'; so that the reader feels himself 'a life prisoner, but reconciled.'"

NOVEMBER
16

NOVEMBER
17

1889 Playwright and wit George S. Kaufman—among whose sparkling creations (many of them written in collaboration with others) are *You Can't Take It With You, The Man Who Came to Dinner, Of Thee I Sing*, and *The Solid Gold Cadillac*—is born in Pittsburgh.

COVARRUBIAS

George S. Kaufman by Covarrubias. Prints and Photographs Division.

NOVEMBER
18

Allen Tate. Photo by Gerald Holly—The Nashville Tennessean.

1847 Humorist, essayist, and illustrator Clarence Day, author of *Life with Father*, is born in New York City.

1865 "Jim Smiley and His Jumping Frog" appear on the pages of the New York *Saturday Press* and quickly leap into the American imagination. This story, now known as "The Celebrated Jumping Frog of Calaveras County," makes its author, Mark Twain, famous.

1911 Sociological writer and humorist Ruth McKenney, who wrote *My Sister Eileen* about her sister, Eileen, is born in New York City.

NOVEMBER
19

1863 President Abraham Lincoln and celebrated orator Edward Everett deliver speeches at the dedication of a military cemetery in Gettysburg, Pennsylvania. Lincoln's speech—very short, and at the time dismissed as "dull and commonplace"—becomes one of the best-known and oft-quoted pieces of American oratory.

1899 Poet, essayist, biographer, and novelist Allen Tate—Library of Congress Consultant in Poetry 1943–44—is born in Clarke County, Kentucky. "I have been asked many times why I became a writer. I simply could not put my mind on anything else. As far back as I can remember I was wondering why the people and families I knew —my own family particularly—had got to be what they were, and what their experience had been. This problem, greatly extended, continues to absorb all my study and speculation. . . ."

1870 Novelist Mary Johnston—author of *To Have and To Hold*, a story of early days in Virginia, and *The Great Valley*, one of the best stories of capture by and escape from Indians that has been written—is born in Buchanan, Virginia.

1905 Poet, critic, and translator Kenneth Rexroth *(The Dragon and the Unicorn)*, whose work attacked the dehumanizing forces in modern society, is born in South Bend, Indiana.

СОБРАНІЕ СОЧИНЕНІЙ

МАРКА ТВЭНА

ТОМЪ X.

◄+●+►

С.-ПЕТЕРБУРГЪ.
«Собраніе сочиненій избранныхъ иностранныхъ писателей».
1899.

Title page from an 1899 Russian edition of the collected works of Mark Twain. General collections.

NOVEMBER

24

NOVEMBER

25

1894 Novelist and dramatist *(What Price Glory?)* Laurence Stallings is born in Macon, Georgia.

NOVEMBER

26

NOVEMBER

27

1909 James Agee, author of *A Death in the Family* and *Let Us Now Praise Famous Men*, is born in Knoxville, Tennessee.

Tomo!«
Ni otkle odgovora.
»Tomo!«
Ni otkle odgovora.
»Čudno mi je, što se dogodilo s tim dječakom? Tomo!« Stara gospođa spusti naočali i pogleda iznad njih po sobi, a onda ih opet potisne na čelo i pogleda ispod njih. Ona nije gotovo nikada gledala k r o z njih na tako neznatnu stvar, kao što je jedan dječak, ta ovo su bile njene svečane naočali, ponos njena srca; nosila ih je više zbog »stila«, a ne da joj služe; upravo bi tako mogla gledati kroz par koluta sa štednjaka. Časkom se zbunila, a onda rekla ne baš ljutito, ali dosta jasno, da bi je moglo čuti pokućtvo u sobi:

»Dobro, dobro, ako te ja uhvatim, ja ću — — — «

Nije ni dovršila, već se sagnula i stala gurkati metlom ispod postelje, da se sva zaduvala. Istjerala je napolje samo mačku.

»Je li itko još vidio takvoga dečka !«

Opening page from a Yugoslav edition of Mark Twain's Tom Sawyer, *1926 (opposite). General collections.*

NOVEMBER 28

1894 Dramatic critic, essayist, and traveler Brooks Atkinson *(Skyline Promenades, Thoreau: The Cosmic Yankee, Broadway Scrapbook)* is born in Melrose, Massachusetts. Best known as a sensitive and scholarly critic of the stage, Atkinson was not averse to lowering the boom when a play did not measure up to his standards—*Thanks for Tomorrow*, for example: "Thanks for tomorrow, thanks for last week, thanks for next Friday—in fact, thanks for everything except last night."

NOVEMBER 29

1799 Amos Bronson Alcott—educator, author, mystic, philosopher ("the most transcendental of the Transcendentalists"), and father of Louisa May Alcott—is born on a farm at Spindle Hill near Wolcott, Connecticut.

1832 Louisa May Alcott, author of *Little Women*, is born in Germantown, Pennsylvania, on her father's birthday.

NOVEMBER 30

1835 Samuel Langhorne Clemens, who will achieve fame as Mark Twain, is born in Florida, Missouri. "My books are water; those of the great geniuses are wine. Everybody drinks water."

Illustration by Dan Beard from Mark Twain's A Connecticut Yankee in King Arthur's Court, *1889. Cabinet of American Illustration, Rare Book and Special Collections Division.*

DECEMBER

1

1886 Rex Stout—creator of the elephantine, hypochondriac, beer-and-orchid-loving detective Nero Wolfe—is born in Nobelsville, Indiana.

DECEMBER

2

Willa *Cather by Covarrubias. Prints and Photographs Division.*

DECEMBER

3

1911 Poet and novelist Kenneth Patchen is born in Niles, Ohio.

DECEMBER

4

1886 Poet Joyce Kilmer, most famous for "Trees" ("Poems are made by fools like me/But only God can make a tree"), is born in New Brunswick, New Jersey.

1873 Willa Cather, author of *O Pioneers!*, *My Antonia*, and *Death Comes to the Archbishop*, is born in Winchester, Virginia. "Artistic growth is, more than it is anything else, a refining of the sense of truthfulness. The stupid believe that to be truthful is easy; only the artist, the great artist, knows how difficult it is."

Willa Cather, January 1936. Photograph by Carl van Vechten. Prints and Photographs Division.

1889 Novelist, poet, and biographer Hervey Allen is born in Pittsburgh. Allen will write *Anthony Adverse*, which will be, until the appearance of *Gone with the Wind*, the best-selling and most discussed novel of its generation.

Is Sex Necessary? asked humorist and cartoonist James Thurber, born on this day in 1894. Research continues.

DECEMBER 9

1871 Novelist, short story writer, and essayist Charles Macomb Flandrau, whose 1908 book *Viva Mexico*, an account of Mexico under the reign of Diaz, will be called one of the best travel books ever written, is born in St. Paul, Minnesota.

1905 Dalton Trumbo, screenwriter and author of the powerful antiwar novel *Johnny Got His Gun*, is born in Montrose, Colorado.

DECEMBER 10

1830 Emily Dickinson is born in Amherst, Massachusetts.

DECEMBER 11

An 1863 "shape book" edition of Red Riding Hood. Rare Book and Special Collections Division.

DECEMBER 12

1897 Novelist and student of race relations Lillian Smith, author of *Strange Fruit* and *The Winner Names the Age*, is born in Jasper, Florida.

DECEMBER
13

1896 Journalist and political commentator Drew Pearson is born in Evanston, Illinois.

DECEMBER
14

1919 Novelist and short story writer Shirley Jackson is born in San Francisco.

1888 Dramatist and poet Maxwell Anderson—whose plays include *What Price Glory?* (with Laurence Stallings), *Winterset*, *Anne of the Thousand Days*, and *The Bad Seed*—is born in Atlantic, Pennsylvania.

DECEMBER
15

1904 Betty Smith, author of *A Tree Grows in Brooklyn*, is born—in Brooklyn.

1863 Spanish-American philosopher, critic, poet, and novelist George Santayana is born in Madrid.

DECEMBER
16

1901 Anthropologist and author Margaret Mead, author of the classic text *Coming of Age in Samoa* and the autobiography *Blackberry Winter*, is born in Philadelphia.

DECEMBER
17

1807 Poet and editor John Greenleaf Whittier is born near Haverhill, Massachusetts.

1903 Erskine Caldwell, author of *Tobacco Road* and *God's Little Acre*, is born in Coweta County, Georgia.

DECEMBER
18

1901 Oliver La Farge—whose work centers about and speaks on behalf of American Indians—is born in New York City. La Farge won the Pulitzer Prize in 1929 for his first novel, *Laughing Boy.*

1907 H. Allen Smith, author of over 30 books of anecdotal humor and the autobiography *To Hell in a Handbasket*, is born in that section of Illinois known as "Egypt."

DECEMBER
19

DECEMBER
20

1830 Mary Virginia Terhune, novelist, writer on household management *(Common Sense in the Household)*, and mother of writer Albert Payson Terhune, is born in Amelia County, Virginia.

1872 Albert Payson Terhune—journalist, novelist, and writer of animal stories *(Lad, a Dog, Collie to the Rescue)*—is born in Newark, New Jersey.

DECEMBER
21

1839 Hezekiah Butterworth—best known as a writer for young people and author of 17 volumes of *Zig Zag Journeys*—is born in Warren, Rhode Island. In 1885 he will write in his journal: "Resolved, it is my purpose to give my whole heart and thought to my work with the pen and to write only that which will tend to make my readers better in heart and life and richer in spiritual knowledge"

1869 Poet Edwin Arlington Robinson, author of "Miniver Cheevy" and "Richard Cory," is born in Head Tide, Maine.

" And thus we die,
Still searching, like poor old astronomers
Who totter off to bed and go to sleep
To dream of untriangulated stars. "

DECEMBER
22

1823 Two days before Christmas "The Night Before Christmas" by Clement Clark Moore is published in the Troy, New York, *Sentinel* under the title "A Visit from St. Nicholas."

1923 Novelist Calder Willingham is born in Atlanta, Georgia.

DECEMBER
23

1851 Librarian of Congress John Silva Meehan writes Senator James A. Pearce: "It is my melancholy duty to inform you that a fire originated in the principal room of the Library of Congress this morning, about half past seven o'clock, and that nearly everything in the room was destroyed before the flames were subdued." The fire destroyed approximately 35,000 of the Library's 55,000 volumes, including nearly two-thirds of Thomas Jefferson's library.

*A*nnually—An eccentrically designed Reindeer-powered Flying Object which tends to land often (always near chimneys), inspires creativity in untold numbers of authors, while others are moved to recite previously existing literature on the phenomenon.

DECEMBER
24

"In Santa Claus's Workshop," from Harper's Young People, *1889. General collections.*

IN SANTA CLAUS'S WORKSHOP.
CLOWN. "WHAT'S THE MATTER NOW?"
SANTA CLAUS. "I'M HAVING SOME DIFFICULTY IN PLACING THIS OTHER EYE."
CLOWN. "WELL, PUT ON MY ARMS FIRST, AND I'LL HELP YOU."

1760 The first publication by an African-American writer appears on this date. *An Evening Thought. Salvation by Christ, with Penetential Cries* by Jupiter Hammon is published as a broadside.

*A*nnually—Gaily wrapped packages appear under trees, which appear in living rooms. Coal materializes in selected stockings. Much literature is devoted to connecting these phenomena with the RFO (see December 24th).

1891 Henry Miller—author of *Tropic of Cancer*, *The Air-Conditioned Nightmare*, and *The Rosy Crucifiction* trilogy—is born in New York City. "My aim in writing is to establish a greater *reality.* I am at bottom a metaphysical writer, and my use of drama and incident is only a device to posit something more profound. Above all, I am for imagination, fantasy, for a liberty as yet undreamed of."

Gambler of the West *from the dime novel collection, Rare Book and Special Collections Division.*

References

A vast number of excellent books dealing with the particulars of America's literary history have been published through the years. The Library of Congress includes many hundreds of these in its collections. Those listed below have been particularly valuable in garnering the names, dates, anecdotes, and quotations included in this book of days:

Bartlett, John, and Emily Morison Beck, ed. 1968. *Familiar Quotations*, Fourteenth Edition. Boston: Little, Brown and Company. [Quotations on 1/11, 1/17, 1/19, 1/24, 2/16, 2/22, 2/23, 2/27, 3/1 (Howells), 4/30, 5/5 (Lewis), 5/27, 6/1, 7/4, 7/9, 7/11, 7/12, 7/21, 7/29 (Tarkington, Marquis), 8/1, 8/22, 8/29, 9/7, 9/16, 9/24, 9/25, 9/26, 10/2, 10/3, 10/11, 10/18 (Smith), 12/7]

Benet's *Readers' Encyclopedia*, third edition. 1987. New York: Harper & Row.

Brittain, Robert, ed. 1986. *The Booklover's Almanac*. New York: Frederic C. Beil. [Quotations on 4/26, 6/5, 7/7]

Carruth, Gorton. 1987. *The Encyclopedia of American Facts & Dates*. New York: Harper & Row.

Cole, John Y. 1979. *For Congress and the Nation: A Chronological History of the Library of Congress*. Washington, DC: Library of Congress. [Quotations on 1/16, 2/21, 2/24, 12/24]

David, Thadious M., and Trudier Harris, ed. 1984. *Afro-American Fiction Writers After 1955* (Dictionary of Literary Biography, Vol. 33). Detroit: Gale Research Co. [Quotation on 2/18]

Jones, Neal T. 1984. *A Book of Days for the Literary Year*. New York: Book-of-the-Month Club, Inc. (First published in the United States by Thames and Hudson.)

Kunitz, Stanley J., and Howard Haycraft. 1973. *Twentieth Century Authors: A Biographical Dictionary of Modern Literature*. New York: The H. W. Wilson Company. [Quotations on 3/6, 3/18, 3/26, 4/11, 5/5 (Morley), 5/15 (Porter), 6/6, 6/26, 7/14, 7/15, 8/8, 11/19 (Tate), 11/28, 12/26]

Kunitz, Stanley J. 1979. *Twentieth Century Authors: A Biographical Dictionary of Modern Literature*, First Supplement. New York: The H. W. Wilson Company. [Quotations on 1/6, 2/2, 2/9, 2/25, 3/1 (Wilbur), 4/13, 5/17, 6/21, 6/23, 7/23, 7/26 (Gallico), 8/31, 9/5, 9/17, 9/30, 10/4, 10/9, 10/14, 10/17, 11/5, 11/6, 11/15]

MacDonald, John D. 1987. *Reading for Survival*. Washington, DC: Library of Congress. [Quotation on 7/24]

Platt, Suzy, ed. 1989. *Respectfully Quoted: A Dictionary of Quotations Requested from the Congressional Research Service*. Washington, DC: Library of Congress.

Rood, Karen L., ed. 1988. *American Literary Almanac*. New York: Facts on File. [Quotations on 5/15 ("Terry Mack"), 8/15, 8/23, 8/30]

Shapiro, Larry. 1987. *A Book of Days in American History*. New York: Book-of-the-Month Club, Inc. (Originally published by Charles Scribner's Sons, New York.)

All illustrations used in this book are from the collections of the Library of Congress.

Index

References to illustrations appear in italic.